Introducing
Craft Design & Technology

ANDREW BRECKON & DAVID PREST

THAMES/HUTCHINSON

Hutchinson & Co. (Publishers) Ltd

An imprint of the Hutchinson Publishing Group

17–21 Conway Street, London W1P 6JD

Hutchinson Group (Australia) Pty Ltd
30–32 Cremorne Street, Richmond South, Victoria 3121
PO Box 151, Broadway, New South Wales 2007

Hutchinson Group (NZ) Ltd
32–34 View Road, PO Box 40–086, Glenfield, Auckland 10

Hutchinson Group (SA) (Pty) Ltd
PO Box 337, Bergvlei 2012, South Africa

First published 1983 by
Hutchinson & Co. (Publishers) Ltd
in association with Thames Television International Ltd
149 Tottenham Court Road, London W1P 9LL

© Andrew Breckon and David Prest 1983

Designed and illustrated by The New Book Factory, London
Typeset in 10½pt Meridien by Parkway Illustrated Press, Abingdon
Printed in Great Britain by The Anchor Press Ltd
and bound by Wm Brendon & Son Ltd
both of Tiptree, Essex

British Library Cataloguing in Publication Data

Breckon, Andrew
   Introducing Craft, Design and Technology.
   1. Handicrafts — Study and teaching
   2. Design — Study and teaching
   3. Technology — Study and teaching
   I. Title   II. Prest, David
   607   TT150

ISBN 0 09 149541 5

Acknowledgements
The authors would like to thank the following for their help in the preparation of this book: students from Middlesex Polytechnic especially: Geoff Pragnell for cartoon ideas on pp. 6, 8 and 9, Linda Farneaux for rocking horse on p. 27, Irene Coles for box on p. 27, Tom Brown for etched tray on p. 29, Chris Cox for acrylic camel on cover and p. 35; pupils from the School of St David and St Katharine, Hornsey and the William Forster School, Tottenham; Christine Prest for typing up the manuscript.

Acknowledgement is also due to the following for permission to reproduce photographs: Heather Angel: wasps' nest and badger skull p. 28, honeybee, earthworm and moorhen's feet p. 44, spider and hop plant p.45; British Railways Board: logo p. 26; Crafts Council: painted face p. 34; ERA Technology Ltd: magnified paper clip p. 29; E. Glover: carved bowl p. 42; Kanehara Shuppan Co. Ltd: colour blindness test chart p. 35; reproduced by gracious permission of Her Majesty the Queen: Leonardo da Vinci drawings p. 7; Mary Evans Picture Library: Leonardo da Vinci drawings p. 7; Plessey Semiconductors: electronic components on cover; D. Pye: wooden bowl p. 29; Royal National Institute for the Blind: reading braille p. 29; Thorn EMI Ferguson Ltd: Hi-fi system p. 27; Dave Williams: design drawings on cover and p. 14.

CONTENTS

Craft, Design and Technology

What is Craft, Design and Technology? Is it a new school subject? Is it three different subjects? Or is it one subject which involves a range of knowledge and skills? Will knowing about Craft, Design and Technology be useful to you in the future? Can *anybody* learn how to design? Or is it something that only a few people can do? These are just some of the questions answered in this book.

The subject

Craft, Design and Technology is about designing and making things. It is not really new, although the title may be new in your school.

Things are usually designed and made to help meet real needs. It may be a simple problem like how to hold paper together cheaply (*solution:* a paper clip). Or it may be a difficult problem like how to get things into space (*solution:* a space shuttle). All around you, you will find things which have been designed to solve problems. Sometimes the solutions are very good and clever. And sometimes they do the job, but only just. And sometimes unfortunately, they fail.

Craft, Design and Technology is not concerned just with how things work (**technology**). It is also about how things look (**aesthetics**), and how things 'feel' (**emotions**). It is easy to design and make a simple chair, but it may be uncomfortable and look ugly. It is much better to make a chair that is comfortable *and* looks attractive.

This book explains many of the skills and abilities you need to become a good designer. It also helps you to be aware of good design.

How to use this book

Each chapter introduces different aspects of designing and making. At the back of the book there are projects for you to try. They use the skills and information in the rest of the book. Remember always that it is the *linking together* of all of these areas that leads to really successful solutions.

Look out for things which are well designed. Collect interesting pictures of designs in newspapers and magazines, or sketch things you see. You might find it helpful to keep them all together in a file. Perhaps you could divide this into sections, like the chapters in this book.

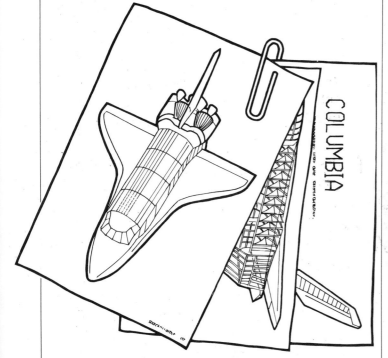

The Taj Mahal is a very good example of Craft, Design and Technology. The designer has combined all the skills and abilities necessary to produce one of the seven great wonders of the world.

Evolution

Humans started to design and make simple tools, shelters and clothes a very long time ago. But even before that, animals and plants had been adapting to various needs and conditions. This process is known as **evolution**. They were evolving solutions to problems set by nature.

Problem: What shape of beak is best for the type of food that a bird eats?

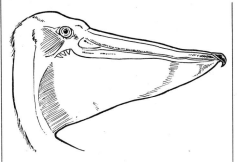

The **pelican** eats fish: it traps them inside its pouch-like beak.

The **curlew** digs for food in deep mud: it has a long, narrow, curved, sharp beak.

The **cockatoo** cracks nuts: it has a powerful hooked beak.

The **vulture** eats small animals: it has a strong hooked beak to tear flesh.

The **kingfisher** catches fish: it has a pointed beak to pick them up.

The **duck** scoops food from mud and water: it has a flat, shovel-like beak.

Problem: How should seeds be protected and spread around?

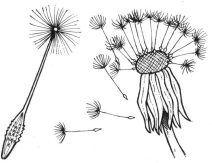

Dandelion seeds have hairy parachutes: the wind carries them for miles.

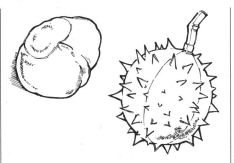

Horse chestnut seeds are protected by a thick, spiky case.

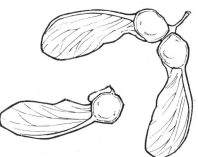

Sycamore seeds have wings, so they fly through the air.

Burdock seeds have hooks: they catch on the fur of animals or the feathers of birds.

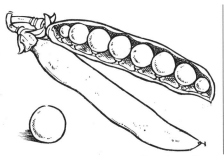

Peas are protected by a pod: when they are ripe, the pod explodes and scatters them.

Poppy seeds fall from the plant when it is shaken by the wind: the wind then scatters them.

First principles

How did early man set about moving large blocks of stone? He did not have previous solutions, or mechanical aids such as cranes and lorries. He had to start from **first principles**. He could use what he already knew about the problem. He could use available technology. And he could use his brain. He probably tackled the problem in stages. They may have been something like this.

Leonardo da Vinci

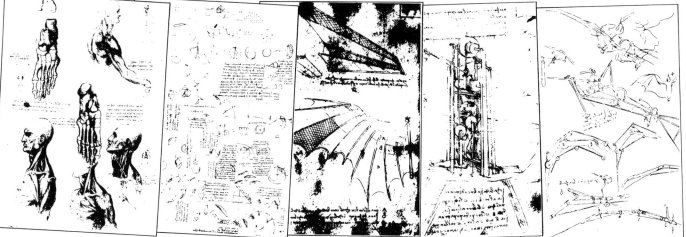

Good design brings together all sorts of information and skills to solve each problem. One of the first people to realize this was Leonardo da Vinci. He lived from 1452 to 1519, and was famous as an artist, a scientist and a designer. He learnt a lot by looking at things (**observing**) and by thinking about them (**analysing**). Then he used this knowledge in solving problems of painting, building and engineering.

Figure 1 shows Leonardo's careful drawings of a human skeleton. He wanted to understand how it was made and how it worked. Some of the drawings show the same things from different angles. The rib cage is drawn looking from the back, from the side and from the front. The legs are drawn from the front and from the side. Leonardo wanted to record how the knee works, and there is a separate drawing of a kneecap.

Figure 2 shows Leonardo's ideas about how to make cogs and pulleys. He kept drawing things he could see, using the nearest piece of paper. On the same page as the cogs are two other sketches – one of a horse's leg muscles, the other of a human face.

Leonardo teaches us to look at what is about us, and to record it in pictures and words. He also reminds us that all knowledge is related. We may divide it into science, mathematics, geography, history and art, but it is all useful in design.

Figure 1

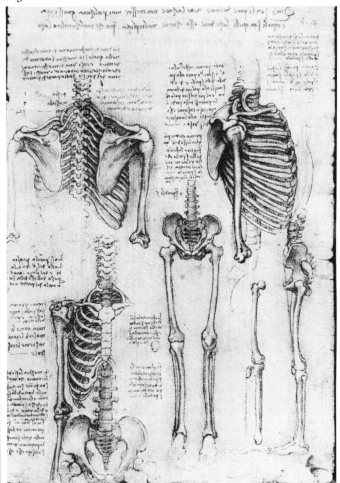

Figure 2

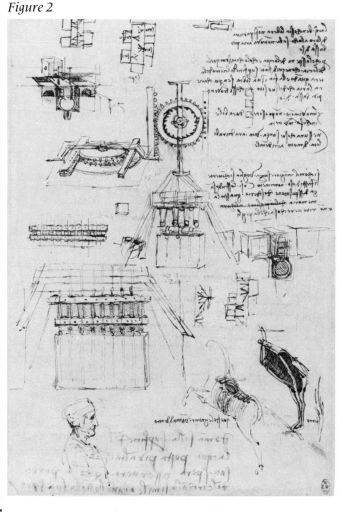

Design and mass production

Man gradually learnt more about tools, materials and principles of technology. He also learnt more about what other people wanted and needed. He could think about problems in new ways.

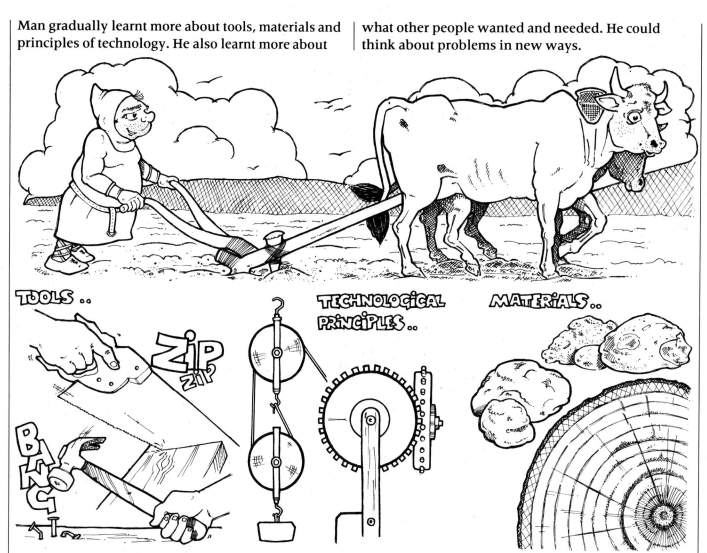

TOOLS .. ZIP ZIP

TECHNOLOGICAL PRINCIPLES ..

MATERIALS ..

BANG

At first, the people who designed things also made them. So the designer knew about the problem and about the materials used to solve it. This helped to make a good, workable solution.

But around 1800 the **Industrial Revolution** changed this. Some people designed things, and different people made them. This made it hard for the designer to know everything about the materials available. Sometimes the designer did not understand how the maker worked. This led to some difficulties.

Items used to be made one at a time by hand. These are described as **hand-made.** Now machinery makes many of them at the same time and much faster. This process is called **mass production.**

Problems of design

Since the Industrial Revolution our knowledge and understanding of technology has developed extremely quickly. The problems that now face designers and society are more varied. Not only do designers have to design goods but they also have to consider what effect producing these goods will have on society. It is up to designers and society to decide to what use our technological knowledge and abilities should be put.

BUZZZz

United States

USA

We can now see how important it is for us as possible designers of the future and members of society to have a clear knowledge and awareness of how the design process works, and how design influences the way in which we live.

Stages of design

The process of designing can be complicated. Many different types of information can be useful in solving a problem. When you are designing something, it is often helpful to split the process into easy stages.

The next few pages show one way of setting about designing something. It is not the only way. Remember that you need to solve different kinds of problem in different ways.

The need

The **need** is where you start. It may be a need or problem that affects only one person. For example, it may be a piece of jewellery, or an aid for a handicapped person. Or it may be something that affects many people. For example, they may need a machine to weigh ingredients for cooking, or the right sort of chair for a waiting room.

Wherever there are people, there are problems needing solutions. And each type of problem will have to be tackled in the right way.

The design brief

It is important for the designer to have a clear statement of the problem he is to solve. This statement is called the **design brief.**

Suppose you have a problem. If you yourself are not going to design the solution, you must give a brief to the designer. But even if *you* are going to design the solution, it is a good idea to write a design brief for yourself. It is like asking a question and then thinking about the answer. The design brief will help you to remember the problem exactly.

The design brief must be short and complete. It must give all the information available about the problem. It must list all the things to be thought about. It is up to the designer to solve the problem, so the design brief must not give any answers, only information.

When you start designing things, you will need very detailed design briefs. These will tell you about what tools and materials to use. But you will soon become more confident and will not need so much information before you start.

Thinking and researching

Once you have the design brief, you must decide how to tackle the problem. Here is one way.

★ *Write down all the information that you think may help you. Write it down as you think of it. There is no need for it to be in any special order.*
★ *Ask your friends to give you any other information that they can think of.*
★ *Then think about the following questions.*

1 **Time** How long have you got to solve the problem?

2 **Materials** What is *available* to you? How much does it *cost*?

3 **Function** What exactly is the article for?

4 **Ergonomics** How big and what shape must the article be? It needs to be comfortable, easy and efficient to use.

5 **Appearance** How will it look?

6 **Technology** Can you make it work?

7 **Safety** Will it be dangerous to use?

8 **Construction** Can you make it?

9 **Society** What are the consequences of making this article?

These questions may lead to other ones for you to think about.

★ *When you have thought about all this, you will need to collect more information. You can also look to see if other people have found solutions to the same problem. You will be able to get information from:*

Museums These may have special collections of natural history or science.

Libraries These may have magazines as well as books. Ask the librarian for help.

Video recordings Such as the programs linked to this book.

Experts Talk to people at schools, colleges and in local industries.

It is important to keep a record of everything you find out, so that you can look at it again later.

Stages of design

NEED ..

BOILED EGG IS HOT AND FALLS OVER!

PERSON IN AGONY HOLDING HOT EGG!

EGG ON PLATE FALLS OVER AND ROLLS ABOUT!

THE DESIGN BRIEF ..

Design and construct a holder for a boiled egg that will enable it to be eaten whilst still hot.

THINKING ..

RESEARCHING ..

101 WAYS TO USE AN EGG

DESIGNS FOR THE IRON BRIDGE

BOILED EGG
1. Must be able to hold egg when hot.
2. Egg must not roll about on plate.
3. Egg must stand up.
4. Eggs vary in size.
5. Eggs are fragile.
6. Egg must still be hot to eat.
7. Eggs are often eaten with salt.

Developing ideas

You can now start your own design work, using the information you have gathered. You may produce completely new ideas, or new versions of old ideas. A lot of commercial designs are new forms of earlier designs. But there is a difference between using ideas and copying solutions. A design is not always good just because it is different.

You need to write and draw your ideas on paper. There are three reasons for this:

★ *You have a record that you can come back to.*
★ *Writing and drawing help to make ideas clearer to you.*
★ *It is easier to discuss your ideas with someone else if you have something to look at.*

Some ways of writing and drawing are particularly clear, quick and efficient. These are introduced on pages 14–24.

Your first ideas will not be the final solution. They will need developing. You may want to spend more time on one of them or combine several of them before you pick the best solution.

There is no way of knowing how long this will take – it depends on the problem. But it is usually best to spend quite a long time thinking at this stage. If you think carefully now, you are less likely to have difficulties later.

When you have decided on your solution, look again at the design brief. Make sure that you have solved the original problem.

Planning

What you need now is a careful drawing of your solution. It needs to show all the information about how to make it.

★ *What are the measurements of the article? How long, how wide, how high is it?*

★ *What is it made of?*
★ *How is it made?*
★ *Does it have any special details? Is it finished in a particular way? Is it fitted to anything else?*

Next you should plan how you are going to make the article.

★ *Does it have several parts? If so, which are you going to make first? Think about the best way to use your time. For example, glue takes some time to set, and you could do something else while you are waiting.*
★ *Do you need new skills? Or can you make the article with what you already know?*
★ *How accurate do the measurements have to be? Does it matter if parts of the article are a bit big or a bit small? There are ways of helping you to work accurately. For instance, you might cut out a complicated shape once and use this as a pattern (**template**) to make exact copies.*

Realizing

First you *designed* the article. Then you *planned* how to make it. Now you can actually *make* it. The process of turning the idea on paper into a real article is called **realization**. It means 'making real'.

A good idea may be ruined if the real article is not made carefully according to the design. You need to be very careful as you make and finish the article.

Testing and evaluating

Finally, you need to find out whether your design has really solved the problem. Think about this yourself and ask other people. You may need to make small alterations to your design, or perhaps start again. Very few designs are perfect – there is usually room for improvement.

Stages of design

DEVELOPMENT ..

PLANNING ..

EGG HOLDER
1. Find wood.
2. Find tools.
3. Make top.
4. Have a cup of tea.
5. Make bottom.
6. Join top to bottom.
7. Boil egg.
8. Eat egg using new egg holder.

← FINAL DESIGN

REALIZATION ..

TESTING + EVALUATION ..

1.

2.

3.

Drawing

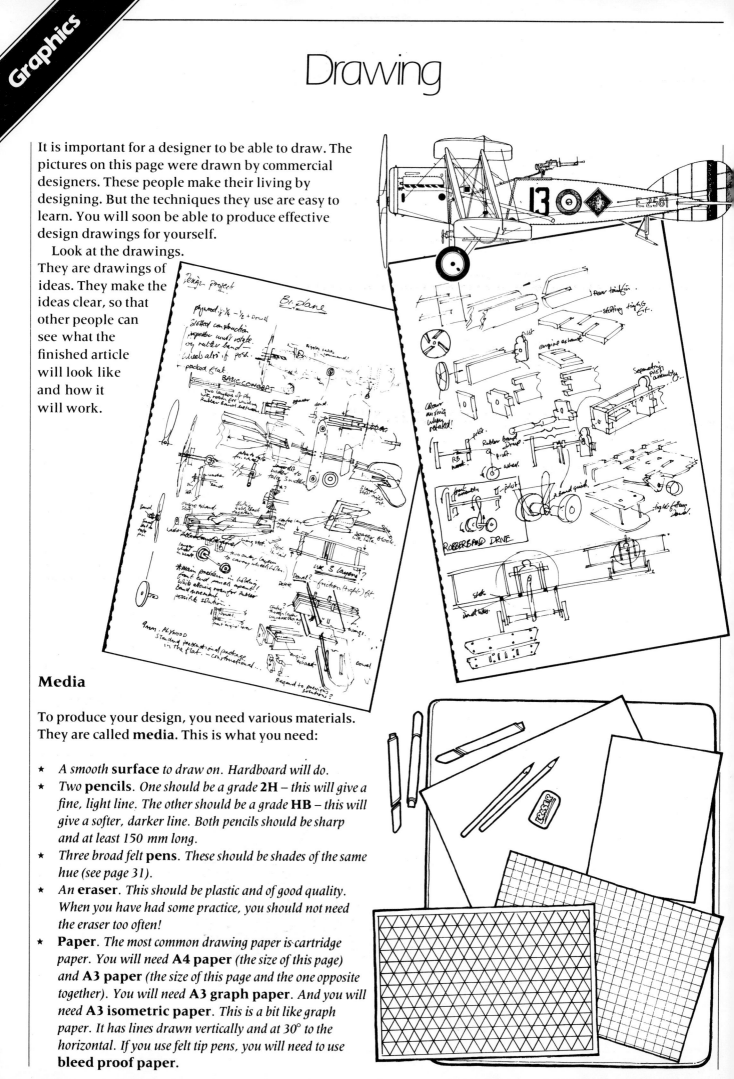

It is important for a designer to be able to draw. The pictures on this page were drawn by commercial designers. These people make their living by designing. But the techniques they use are easy to learn. You will soon be able to produce effective design drawings for yourself.

Look at the drawings. They are drawings of ideas. They make the ideas clear, so that other people can see what the finished article will look like and how it will work.

Media

To produce your design, you need various materials. They are called **media**. This is what you need:

★ *A smooth* **surface** *to draw on. Hardboard will do.*
★ *Two* **pencils**. *One should be a grade* **2H** *– this will give a fine, light line. The other should be a grade* **HB** *– this will give a softer, darker line. Both pencils should be sharp and at least 150 mm long.*
★ *Three broad felt* **pens**. *These should be shades of the same hue (see page 31).*
★ *An* **eraser**. *This should be plastic and of good quality. When you have had some practice, you should not need the eraser too often!*
★ **Paper**. *The most common drawing paper is cartridge paper. You will need* **A4 paper** *(the size of this page) and* **A3 paper** *(the size of this page and the one opposite together). You will need* **A3 graph paper**. *And you will need* **A3 isometric paper**. *This is a bit like graph paper. It has lines drawn vertically and at 30° to the horizontal. If you use felt tip pens, you will need to use* **bleed proof paper**.

Drawing systems

In this chapter we look at three different ways of drawing objects on paper. The wooden block shown in the photograph (*Figure 1*) is also shown drawn in each of these three ways.

If you were to pick the block up and look at it, you would see that it is completely regular. Each face is a rectangle. All the long edges are parallel. But when you stand back and look at it, the lines seem to get closer together as they get further away. The far end of the block *looks* smaller than the near end. This appearance is known as a **perspective** view. You can draw the block to show this perspective using a technique called **two-point perspective drawing** (*Figure 2*).

Another technique is called **isometric drawing** (*Figure 3*). If lines on the real object are parallel, you draw them parallel. If lines are actually the same length, you draw them the same length.

The third technique is called **orthographic projection** (*Figure 4*). In this, you draw the object from several directions as if it was flat. With this method, rectangles actually appear in the drawing as rectangles.

Drawing may be done using instruments such as rulers and compasses. Or it may be done without, by eye. Drawings done without instruments are **freehand** and are quicker.

We shall use the wooden block and the model car (*Figure 5*) to explain the different methods of drawing.

Figure 1

Perspective

Figure 2

Isometric

Figure 3

Orthographic projection

Figure 4

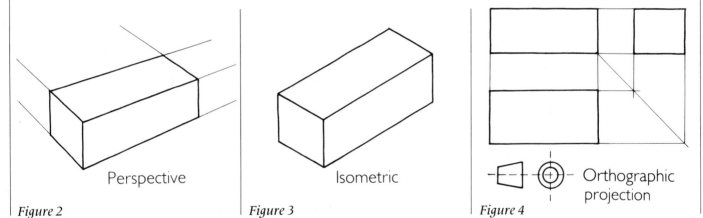

Figure 5

Freehand drawing

We begin with some simple freehand drawing. You need a flat drawing board with straight edges. You also need a piece of A4 cartridge paper and a sharp HB pencil.

To draw a line parallel to a straight edge

★ *Place the paper on the drawing board. The edge of the paper must be along the edge of the board.*

★ *Hold the paper with one hand. Hold the pencil with the other hand, as shown in Figure 1. Rest your middle fingers against the edge of the board. Now draw a line down the edge of the paper. Don't press too hard!*

★ *Do the same thing again for the other three edges of your paper.*

★ *Draw an extra line at the bottom of the paper, so that you make a box. You can write a title in the box.*

To draw other straight lines

★ *Decide where you want to draw the straight line. Make a light dot at the start of the line, and another dot at the end of the line.*

★ *Hold your pencil lightly. Rest your hand on the board. Keep your wrist firm. Place the point of your pencil on the first dot. Don't look at the pencil – look at the second dot. Now join the dots together (Figure 2).*

★ *Draw more dots, and join them together. Practise this several times.*

★ *Now draw six more lines. Draw them all parallel. Make the first line very light. Make the second one a bit darker. Make the third one a bit darker still, and so on. You should be able to make all six lines different. See Figure 5 on the next page.*

★ *The lines you have drawn so far are across the page (**horizontal**). Hold your pencil as shown in Figure 3. Now draw lines which are up and down the page (**vertical**). Make them light and heavy as before (Figure 6).*

★ *Finally, draw six more lines which are slanted across the page (**diagonal**), as shown in Figure 4 (see Figure 7).*

When you draw straight lines, keep your wrist firm. Move the whole of your arm as you draw the line. This will help to make the line smooth and straight. Now you can practise drawing shapes similar to those shown in Figure 8.

To draw a circle, or part of a circle

★ *Decide how big the circle should be. Lightly draw a square just big enough to hold the circle. Mark the middles of the sides – the circle will touch these.*

★ *Hold the pencil as in Figure 3. Keep your wrist firm. Make a circular movement with all of your arm. Touch*

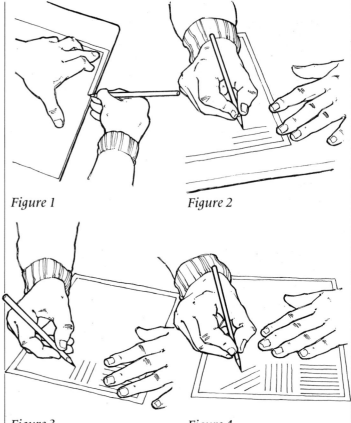

Figure 1   Figure 2

Figure 3   Figure 4

the pencil to the paper, lightly. Keep moving your arm as before. This will produce several light circles in the box (Figure 9).

★ *Choose the best circle from those you have drawn. It should touch the middle of each side of the square. Draw this in more firmly. Make sure that your hand is always on the inside of the curve. To do this, you will have to turn the paper.*

★ *Where the circle touches the square, the curve is just the same. Don't make it pointed anywhere.*

★ *Practise this technique several times. You can use it to draw parts of circles too.*

To draw an ellipse (a circle seen from an angle)

★ *Decide how big the ellipse should be. This time, draw a rectangle instead of a square. Mark the middles of the edges as you did for the circle.*

★ *Draw the ellipse lightly several times, as you did with the circle. Choose the best ellipse and draw this in more firmly (Figure 10).*

★ *Make sure the curve isn't pointed anywhere. The line may be flatter than you expect where it touches the rectangle.*

To draw larger curves (*Figure 11*), use your arm like a pair of compasses. Draw lots of lines like those on the next page. Try drawing shapes like Figure 12.

Freehand drawing

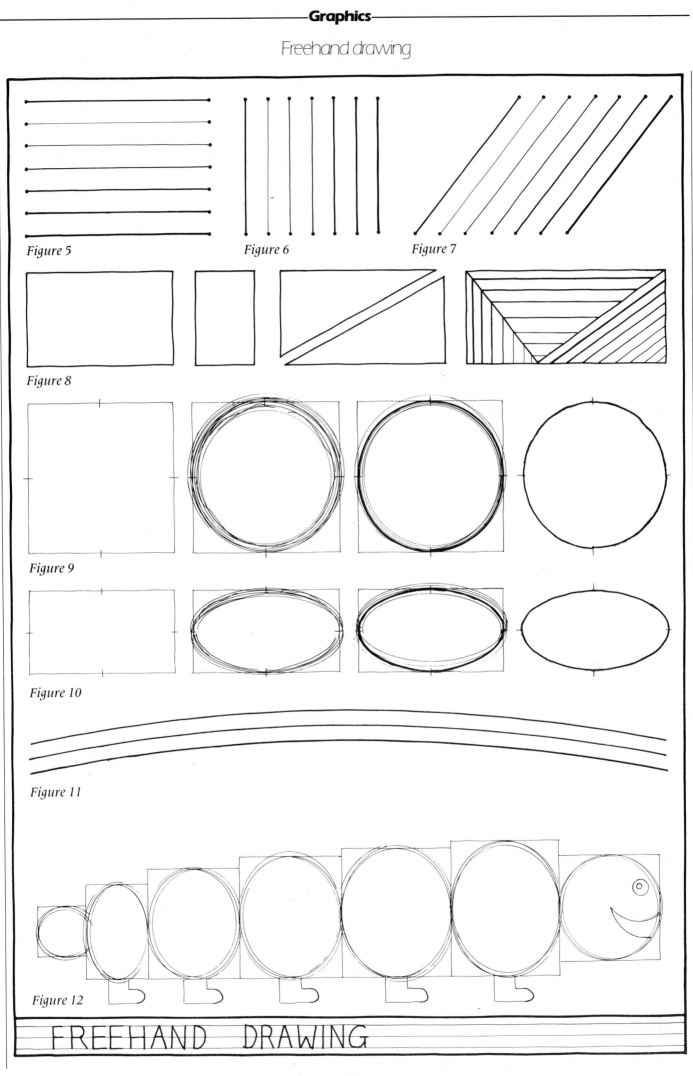

Figure 5

Figure 6

Figure 7

Figure 8

Figure 9

Figure 10

Figure 11

Figure 12

FREEHAND DRAWING

Freehand isometric drawing

This method of drawing is easy to understand. It gives a picture of three sides of an object. The object is drawn like this.

* *Draw one corner at the front of the picture.*
* *Make sure that lines which are vertical on the object are also vertical in the drawing.*
* *Make sure that lines which are horizontal on the object are at 30° to the horizontal in the drawing.*
* *Draw all lines in scale with their true lengths. For example, you might make all lines one quarter of their true length.*

You can make isometric drawings easily with the help of special grid paper. This is shown in the diagrams. You can see how the block is drawn using isometric paper.

When you start, you will draw on the isometric paper itself. But this leaves the grid lines on the final picture. They may confuse someone looking at your drawing. So later on you can draw on plain paper, with the isometric paper underneath it. Then you can see the grid while you are working.

* *First draw the edge of the block nearest to you (Figure 1). Draw it the same length as the actual edge. This is the height of the block.*

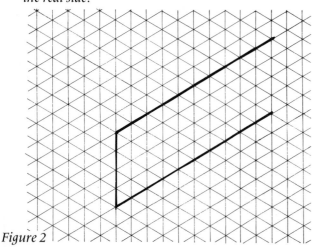

Figure 1

* *Now draw two lines to show the side of the block. These lines are at 30° (Figure 2). They are the same length as the real side.*

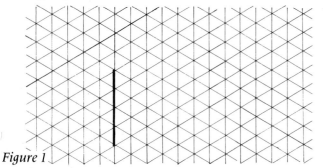

Figure 2

* *Draw two more lines to show the end of the block. These are also at 30°, and they are the true length (Figure 3).*

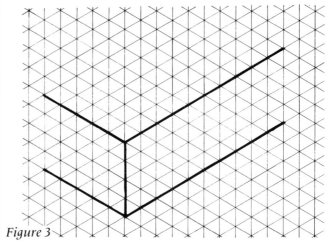

Figure 3

* *Draw the vertical edges at the left and right of the drawing. These are the same height as the block (Figure 4).*

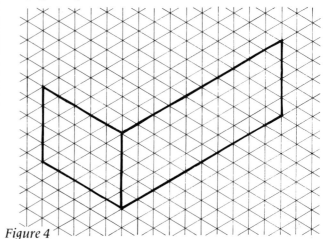

Figure 4

* *Complete the drawing by adding the two top edges. Both are at 30°, and both are the true length (Figure 5).*

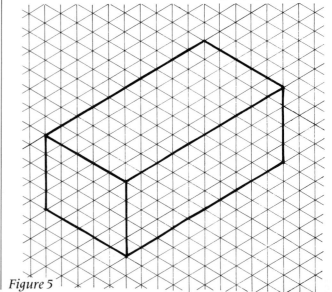

Figure 5

Freehand isometric drawing

You can use isometric drawing to show more complicated shapes. Here is the racing car again, drawn in stages. Notice how the drawing starts with boxes. Even the wheels are drawn as boxes at first.

You can make isometric drawings quite quickly. They give you a useful picture of the object. You can measure parts of the object when you are building it.

But an isometric drawing doesn't look the same as the real object. It looks distorted. This is because all edges are drawn to the true size. When you look at an object, the edges further away from you *seem* smaller. To make drawings look like real objects, you must draw them in a different way, using **perspective**. Artists did not realize this until about 1400 AD.

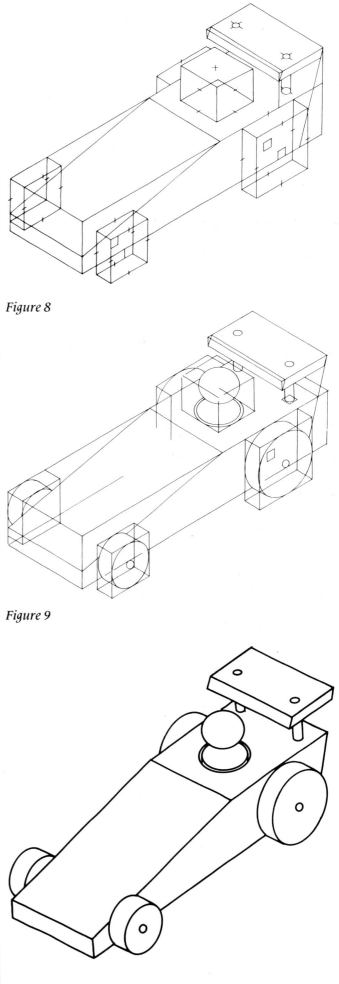

Figure 8

Figure 9

Figure 10

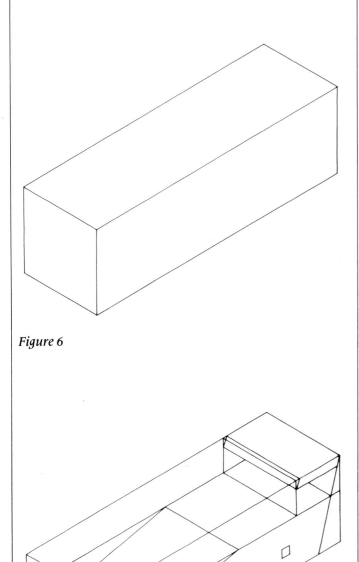

Figure 6

Figure 7

Two-point perspective drawing

Perspective drawing can be done quickly, like isometric drawing.
But the final drawing looks much more like the real object.
   This is the way to draw a perspective view of the block.

★ *Draw a faint line right across the paper (Figure 1). This represents the level of your eyes. As it is a long line, you may need to use a ruler to draw it. Mark points at the ends of the line, near the edge of the paper. These are called* **vanishing points**.

Figure 1

★ *Draw the front vertical edge of the block (Figure 2). This line is the only one drawn to its true length.*

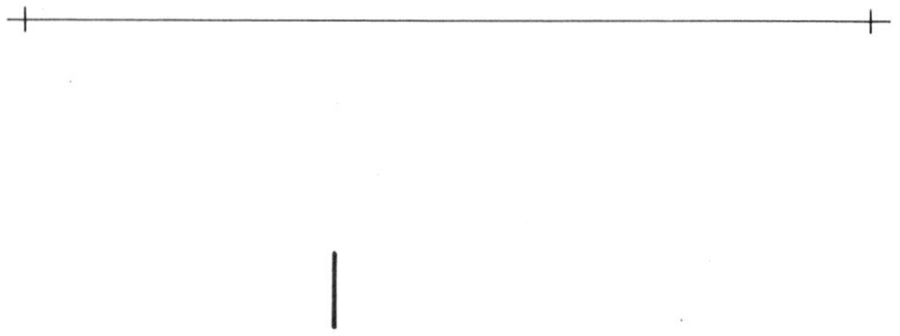

Figure 2

★ *Draw faint lines from the top of the front edge to each of the vanishing points (Figure 3). Do the same for the bottom of the front edge.*

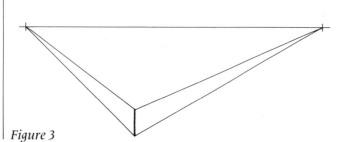

Figure 3

★ *Draw vertical lines to show the back edges of the block (Figure 4). You will have to decide for yourself where to draw these. The length of the sides will be* **smaller** *than on the real object.*

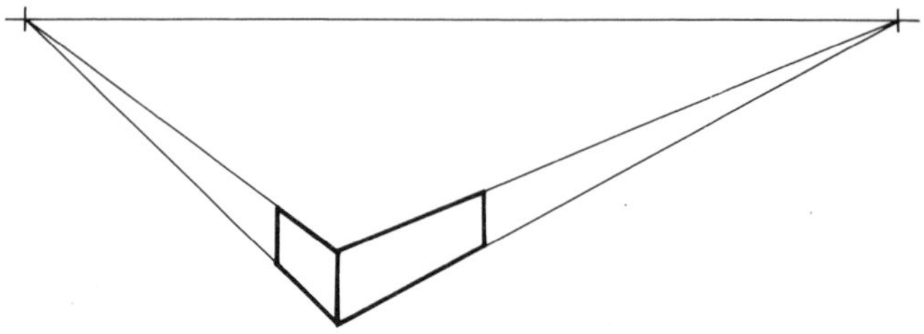

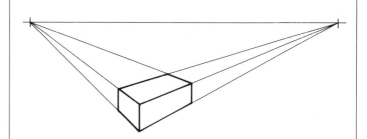

Figure 4

★ *Join the tops of these edges to the vanishing points furthest from them (Figure 5). The two new lines cross at the back corner of the block. Now draw the block in firmly.*

Figure 5

★ *You can draw different views of the block. The front edge can be drawn below the eye level. Or it can be drawn across the eye level. If it is drawn* above *the eye level, you see the bottom of the block (Figure 6).*

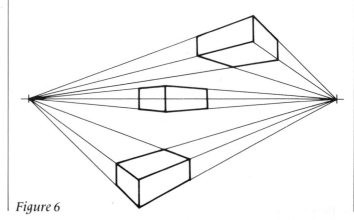

Figure 6

Two-point perspective drawing

You can draw complicated shapes using perspective. It helps if you think of each bit as a box. Then you can make it realistic later.

If the vanishing points are too close together, the picture looks distorted. The pictures here use vanishing points some way off the edges of the paper.

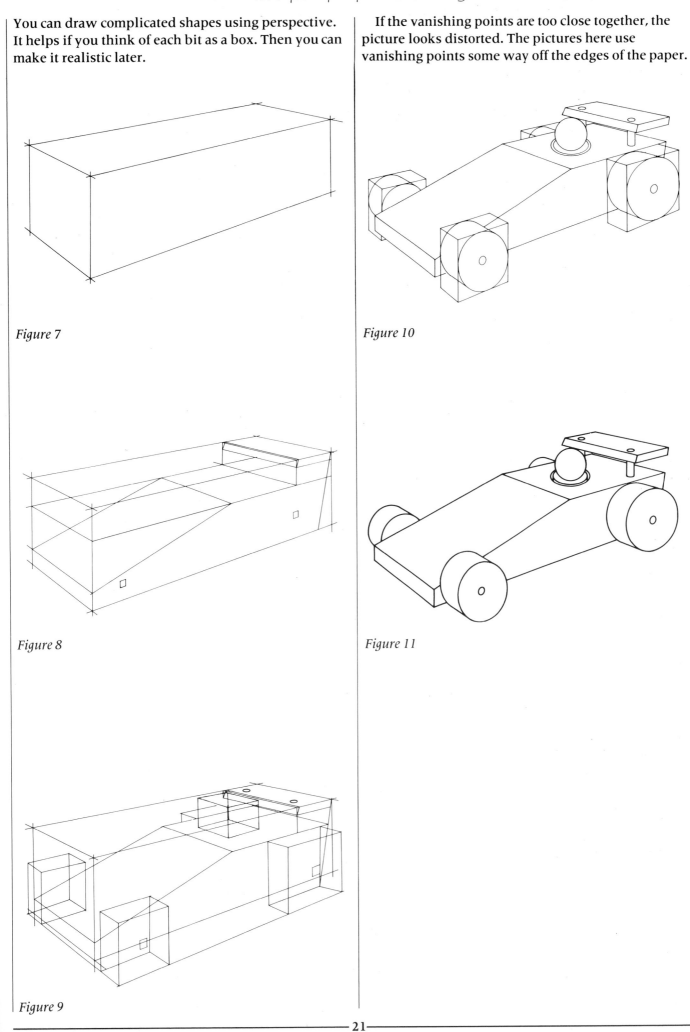

Figure 7

Figure 8

Figure 9

Figure 10

Figure 11

Orthographic projection

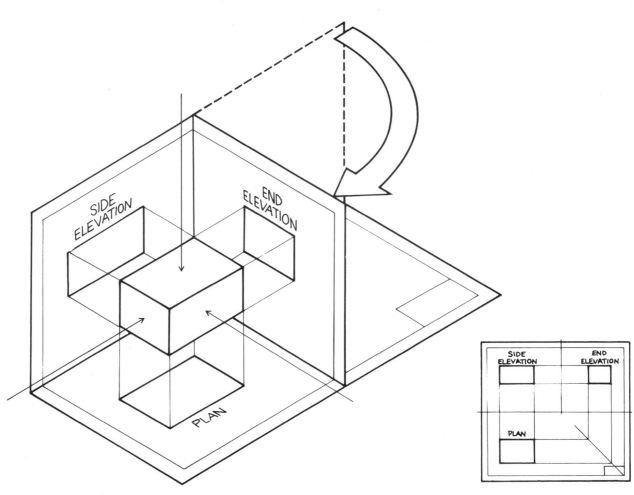

Figure 1

This third method of drawing objects may seem the most complicated. But it is useful, because it gives all the information needed for the object to be made. The other two methods may not give enough information.

An orthographic projection usually shows the object from three points of view (*Figure 1*). They are always positioned in the same way on your drawing paper (*Figure 1*). Anybody can understand the drawing, even if he doesn't speak English.

One view of the object is called the **plan**. It shows everything you would see if you looked at the object from above. The second view is called the **end elevation**. This shows everything you would see if you looked at the object from its end. The third view is called the **side elevation**. This shows the object seen from the side.

You will find it helps to draw orthographic projections on graph paper. Use a 2H pencil to draw the construction lines. Then go over the finished drawing carefully using an HB pencil.

After you have had some practice, you will be able to draw these projections on plain paper. Then you will need a drawing board, a T-square and set squares.

This is the way to draw an orthographic projection of the block.

* *Decide how big the three parts of the drawing will be. This will tell you how to place them on your paper.*
* *Draw a base line across the paper. The side and end elevations will stand on this.*
* *Draw two vertical lines. The distance between them is the same as the length of the block. They show edges of the block on the side elevation and on the plan (Figure 2).*
* *Draw a horizontal line above the base line. The distance between them is the height of the block (Figure 3).*
* *Draw a diagonal line at 45°. (If you are using graph paper, draw the line through the corners of the squares. This line will be at 45°.) The diagonal line must meet the base line to the right of the corner of the side elevation (Figure 4).*
* *Draw one vertical line to the right of the side elevation. Draw it long enough to reach the diagonal. Draw another vertical line further to the right. The distance between them is the width of the end of the block (Figure 5).*
* *Draw horizontal lines to meet the vertical lines where they touch the diagonal (Figure 6).*

Orthographic projection

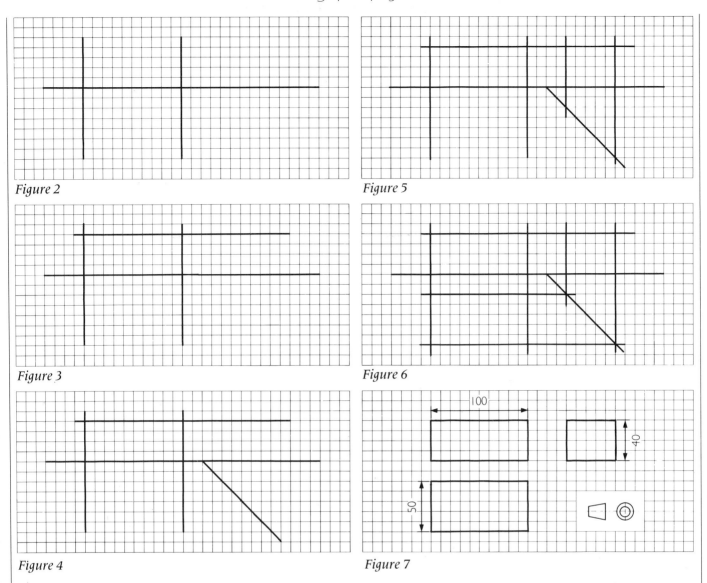

Figure 2

Figure 5

Figure 3

Figure 6

Figure 4

Figure 7

★ *You have now drawn all three views. Line them in with your HB pencil. Add the actual measurements, so that someone else could make the block (Figure 7).*

Orthographic projection is used by lots of people. There are rules that they follow, so that everybody can understand every drawing. The British Standards Institution (BSI) has listed the rules for schools in a booklet called PD 7308.

Look at the orthographic projection of the racing car. Work out how it was drawn. Notice no hidden detail is shown.

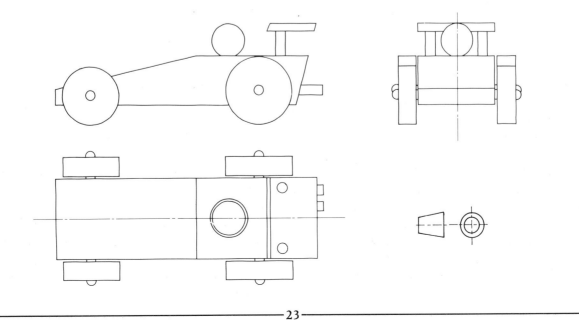

Presentation

Here are some tips that will help you to produce good drawings.

* *Be confident. Drawing is as easy as writing!*
* *Make sure you keep your paper clean. Wash your hands before you start drawing.*
* *Use the correct paper and pencils.*
* *Draw all construction lines lightly.*
* *Line in the finished drawing, with the HB pencil.*
* *Always put a border round the drawing. It makes the drawing look neater.*
* *Practise writing quickly, neatly and clearly. This will make your notes easy to read.*
* *When you make notes on the drawing, use a pencil. If you use a pen the notes seem more important than the drawing, and you can't alter them!*
* *Use neat guidelines when you print headings. This will make sure that all letters are the same height.*
* *Before you start drawing, think about what the finished page will look like. Leave enough room for the parts of the picture and for the notes.*
* *Choose the best drawing method. Think about what you need to show. How will the drawing be used by other people?*
* *Draw the difficult shapes in the picture as boxes first. Then use the box as a guide and make the drawing more realistic.*

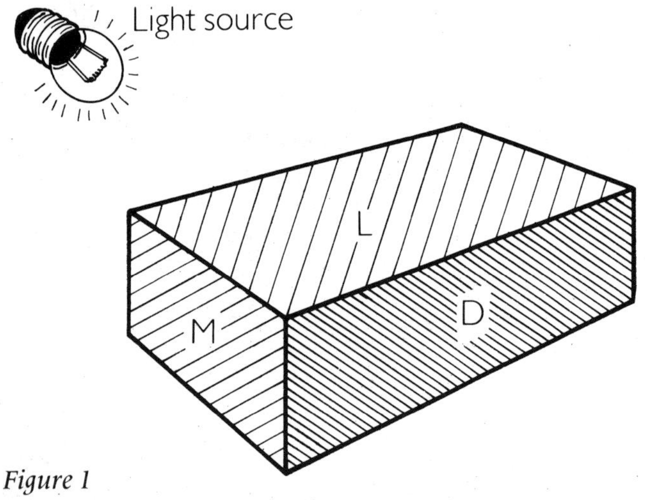

Light source

Figure 1

You can make your drawings stand out from the paper. This is known as giving them **impact**. You can give impact to isometric drawings and to perspective drawings. (Leave orthographic projections as they are, because this makes them more useful to somebody making the object.) Here are some ideas.

* *You could draw round the outside of your picture using a broad-tipped pen or crayon (Figure 1, page 36).*
* *With some sorts of pen and crayon, you could make the edge of the line softer. Use a brush and some clean water (Figure 2, page 36).*
* *You could shade the drawing, using pencil or pens. Imagine that the light in your drawing is coming from behind and to the left. Figure 1 shows how the block is lit. The surface labelled **L** is the lightest, the surface labelled **D** is the darkest, and the surface labelled **M** is medium dark. To produce the different tones using a pencil, you must vary the heaviness and closeness of the lines (Figure 2). To produce the different tones using pens, choose three pens that have different tones of the same colour (Figure 3, page 36).*
* *You could combine these ideas. You could also indicate the material used, for example wood (Figure 4, page 36).*
* *Professional artists have special ways of giving impact to drawings. Look at the perspective drawing of the racing car on page 36. Why does this picture stand out?*

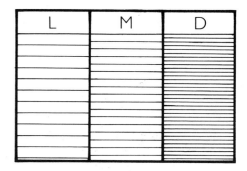

Figure 2

Function and appearance

The most important reason for designing something is to solve a problem that satisfies a need. If you want something to sit on, you design a chair. If you want something to eat food from, you design a plate. But not all chairs are the same, and not all plates are the same. People want you to solve their problems for them. But they also want the solutions – your designs – to be attractive.

A poet called John Keats said that 'A thing of beauty is a joy for ever'. Some people think one thing is beautiful – other people think the same thing is ugly. It is difficult to know why some objects give people pleasure. But you must try to think about this when you design something.

Objects may *look* attractive. Or they may *feel* pleasant. In some designs, other senses are important.

Food must *smell* appetizing and taste good. Music must have a satisfying *sound*. People enjoy the colour of roses, the feel of polished wood, the smell of freshly-ground coffee, the sound of a grand piano.

When you see something you like, work out what you like about it. Is it the shape? Is it the colour? Is it the texture? Or what is it? In the next few pages, we look at some elements of the appearance of objects.

Line

Line can be used to create drawings.
Lines can show what an object will look like when made.
Lines have other uses as well. Below are six pictures: each uses lines.

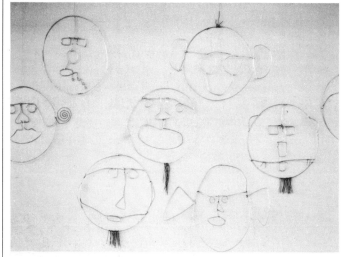

★ *Figure 1 shows faces made of wire. They are two-dimensional. The lines give* shape.

★ *Figure 2 shows a hand, pointing. The lines give* shape *and* direction.

★ *Figure 3 shows two more faces made of wire. They are three-dimensional. The lines give* shape *and* volume.

★ *Figure 4 shows an electricity pylon. The lines give* shape *and* volume.

★ *Figure 5 shows the symbol* (logo) *of British Rail. The lines give* shape. *They also suggest* movement.

★ *Figure 6 shows a very large leaf. The lines give* shape, *and suggest* direction.

Line

Here are some more examples of line.

Figure 7

Figure 8

Figure 9

Figure 10

Figure 11

Figure 12

Figure 13

★ *Figure 7 shows a giraffe. The lines give* pattern.
★ *Figure 8 shows some zebras. The lines give* pattern.
★ *Figure 9 shows a set of hi-fi equipment. The lines here are implied – you can't actually see many of them. Notice that all of the switches, knobs and buttons are in lines. Most of the lines are horizontal. Some lines are vertical.*
★ *Figure 10 shows part of the roof of the Sainsbury Centre in Norwich. The lines give* structure.
★ *Figure 11 shows a bridge, which is made of balsa wood. The lines indicate the* structure *of the bridge. A bridge*

must carry weight. The structure of the bridge determines how big a weight it can carry.
★ *Figure 12 shows a rocking horse. The horse was made from lots of sheets of plywood. As it was shaped, lines began to show. There are lines on some maps that join places of the same height. These are called contour lines. The lines on this rocking horse look like* **contour** *lines. They show* shape *and* form.
★ *Figure 13 shows a cylindrical box. The lines on this suggest* rhythm.

Shape and form

Two more elements of visual design are shape and form. Articles with *two* dimensions (length and breadth) have **shape**. Squares, circles and triangles are shapes. Articles with *three* dimensions (length, breadth and height) have **form**. Cubes, spheres and pyramids are forms.

Some shapes and forms are precise. They are **geometric**. They can be drawn exactly, using rulers, compasses and other instruments. Other shapes and forms are not precise – they are flowing. They may suggest growth. These shapes and forms are **organic**.

Some shapes and forms are made to look very simple. They show only the main features of

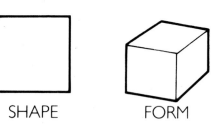

SHAPE   FORM

something, not the detail. These shapes are **stylized**.

Shapes and forms that are solid are described as **positive**. The spaces around them also have shape or form. The spaces are **negative**. Negative shapes are most important when positive shapes are close together.

Geometric shapes and forms

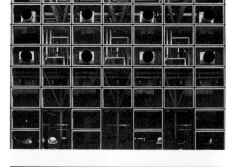
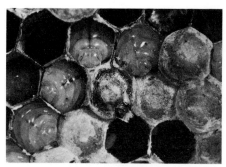

Organic shapes and forms

Stylized shapes and forms

Positive and negative shapes and forms

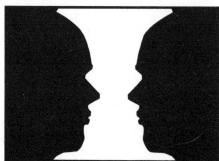

Texture

The next element of visual design is **texture**. Texture is the way a surface feels. For example, glass feels smooth. Glasspaper feels rough. Rock feels hard. Fur feels soft. Surfaces that feel smooth often look very rough when seen through a microscope.

Designers have many different materials to choose from. For example, they can use wood, metal, plastic, glass or fabric. Each has its own texture. Indeed, each can have different textures. There are many kinds of wood, for instance. The texture of each is distinctive.

Materials have texture when you start making something. But you can alter the texture as you make the article. For example, you can make the surface smoother or coarser.

We think of texture as something we *feel*. But it is also something we *see*. A rough surface casts very small shadows. You see the texture because of the contrast between the material and the shadows. The contrast is especially clear if the light is at the side. The brighter the light, the greater the contrast. So the brighter the light, the rougher the surface looks.

Texture is seen because of contrast. Using contrast, we can print on flat surfaces so that they *seem* to be textured. This is often done with wallpaper, for example. Printed paper may be made to look like cloth.

Materials

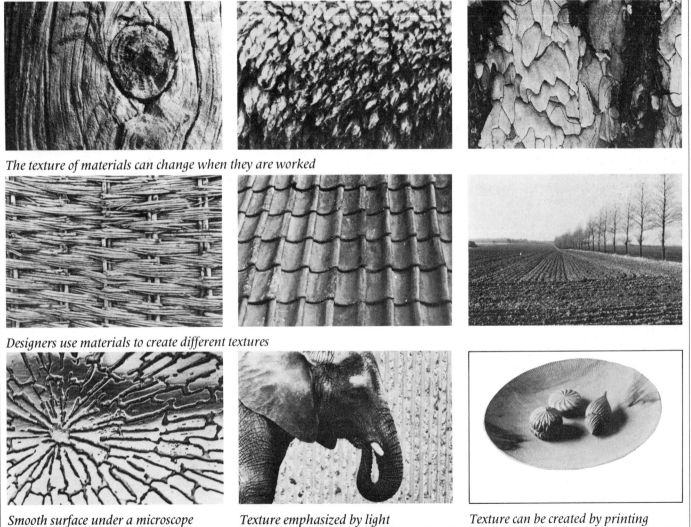

The texture of materials can change when they are worked

Designers use materials to create different textures

Smooth surface under a microscope *Texture emphasized by light* *Texture can be created by printing*

Colour

The final element of visual design is **colour**. The world around you is full of colour. Colour can make things bright or dull. It can make them exciting or boring. It can seem harmonious or harsh. We become used to things being particular colours. Would you enjoy green eggs? Or blue milk? Or a brown sky?

We associate colour with emotion. We say that people are 'green with envy', or 'red with anger'. Designers can use colour to produce particular reactions. They can use colour to shock, to persuade, to frighten or to excite. And they can use colour to explain and to identify. For example, traffic signs with red borders are warnings. Signs with blue backgrounds are for information.

Some people have opinions about combining colours. They may think that blue and white look good together. They may think that red and green clash with each other. But what is right and wrong depends on you. You must decide whether you want to please people or to catch their attention.

We see colour because we shine light on things. Sunlight seems to be white, but really it is a mixture of different colours. If you shine white light through a glass prism, the path of the light is bent. Some colours bend more than others, so the colours separate. Red bends the most. Violet bends the least. The colours form a **spectrum**.

Really, the change from red to violet is gradual. But we usually talk about seven colours that we can see to be different. You can remember them using this sentence:

read over your Greek books in verse
(or) *Richard of York gained battles in vain*

red – orange – yellow – green – blue – indigo – violet

Rain can bend the path of sunlight too. This is why you sometimes see rainbows.

Some people see two colours as the same colour. For example, they may not be able to tell red from green. These people are **colour-blind**. Look at the coloured dots on page 35. What can you see?

Only a few people are colour-blind. But even the rest of us may see colours in slightly different ways.

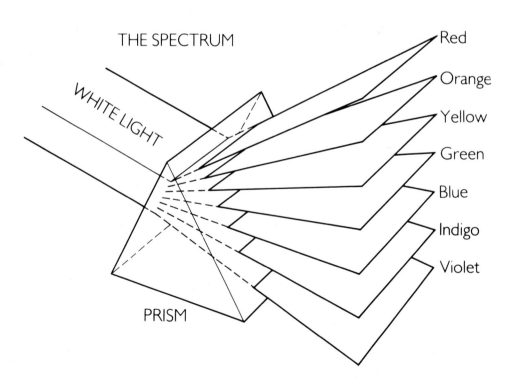

THE SPECTRUM

WHITE LIGHT

PRISM

Red
Orange
Yellow
Green
Blue
Indigo
Violet

Colour

Mixing colours

You can see these in colour on page 33.

PRIMARIES			SECONDARIES		TERTIARIES
red	red + yellow →		orange	red + orange →	red-orange
				yellow + orange →	yellow-orange
yellow	yellow + blue →		green	yellow + green →	yellow-green
				blue + green →	blue-green
blue	blue + red →		violet	blue + violet →	blue-violet
				red + violet →	red-violet

Designers and artists do not often make pictures with light. They use paints, inks, dyes, enamels and resins. These contain natural coloured substances called **pigments**. These behave differently to light.

Three colours are most important – *red, yellow* and *blue*. These are called **primary** colours.

By mixing equal amounts of two primary colours we get a **secondary** colour. There are three secondary colours also. Red and yellow give *orange*. Yellow and blue give *green*. Blue and red give *violet*.

Each secondary colour is made by mixing two primaries. We can mix equal amounts of a secondary and one of the primaries that made it. For example, green is a secondary made with yellow and blue. We can mix green with yellow, to get *yellow-green*. And we can mix green with blue to get *blue-green*. Colours made like this are **tertiary** colours.

These colours can all be arranged in a wheel (page 33). There are the three primaries. Between them are the three secondaries. And between the primaries and the secondaries are the six tertiaries.

These basic colours are called **hues**. In the wheel, they form the middle ring. We can mix the hues with white, making them lighter. The new colours are called **tints**. They are shown in the outer ring. We can also mix the hues with black, making them darker. These new colours are called **shades**. They are shown in the inner ring.

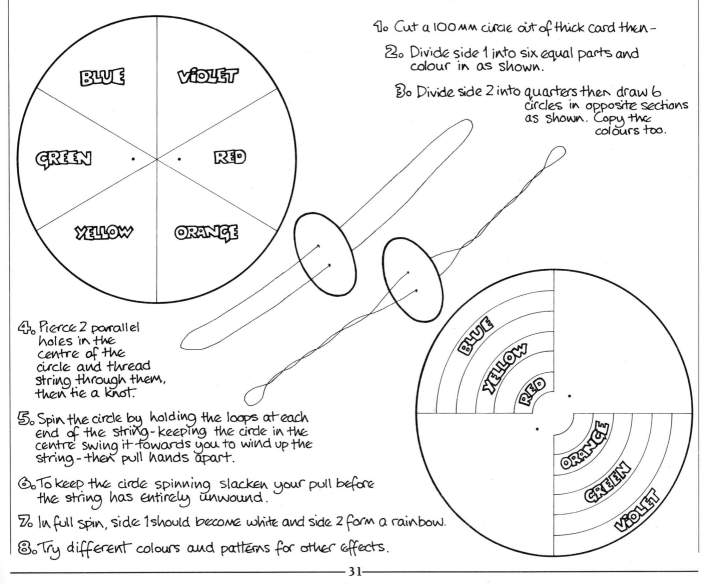

1. Cut a 100 mm circle out of thick card then -

2. Divide side 1 into six equal parts and colour in as shown.

3. Divide side 2 into quarters then draw 6 circles in opposite sections as shown. Copy the colours too.

4. Pierce 2 parallel holes in the centre of the circle and thread string through them, then tie a knot.

5. Spin the circle by holding the loops at each end of the string - keeping the circle in the centre swing it towards you to wind up the string - then pull hands apart.

6. To keep the circle spinning slacken your pull before the string has entirely unwound.

7. In full spin, side 1 should become white and side 2 form a rainbow.

8. Try different colours and patterns for other effects.

Colour

When you choose colours for your design, you may want them to **harmonize**. First you choose a **key colour**. The colours that harmonize with it are the colours next to it on the colour wheel. Or you may want your colours to **contrast** with each other. The greatest contrast is between colours that are opposite each other on the wheel. These colours are **complementary**.

You can use the disc shown below to identify these colours. Trace the drawing onto thin card. Cut out the disc. Then cut out the shaded areas, so that you have four holes. Put the disc over the colour wheel. One hole fits over the key colour. The two holes next to it show the harmonizing colours. The hole opposite shows the complementary colour.

What else can you learn from the colour wheel?

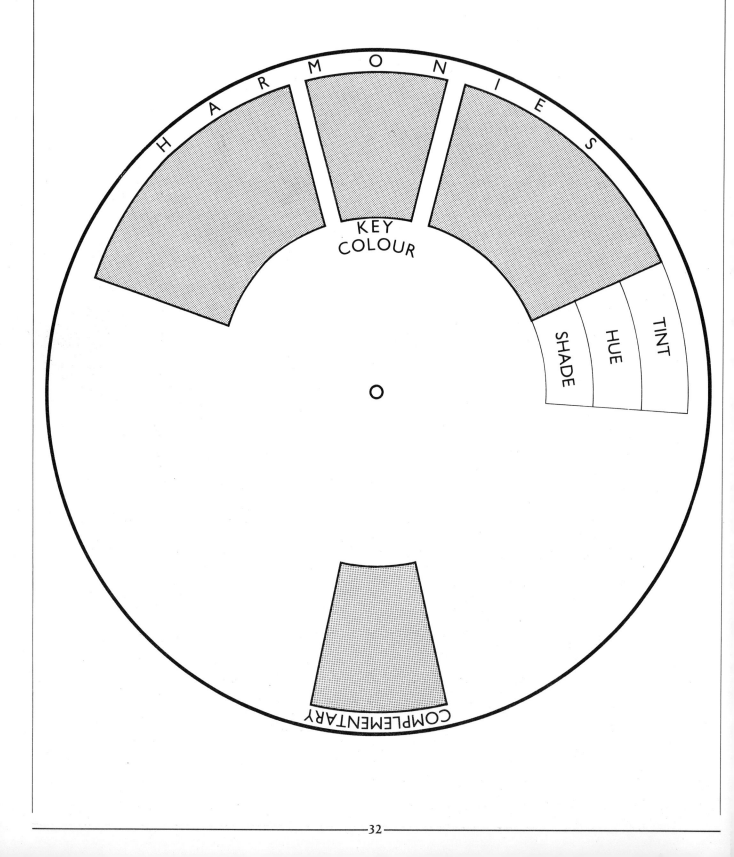

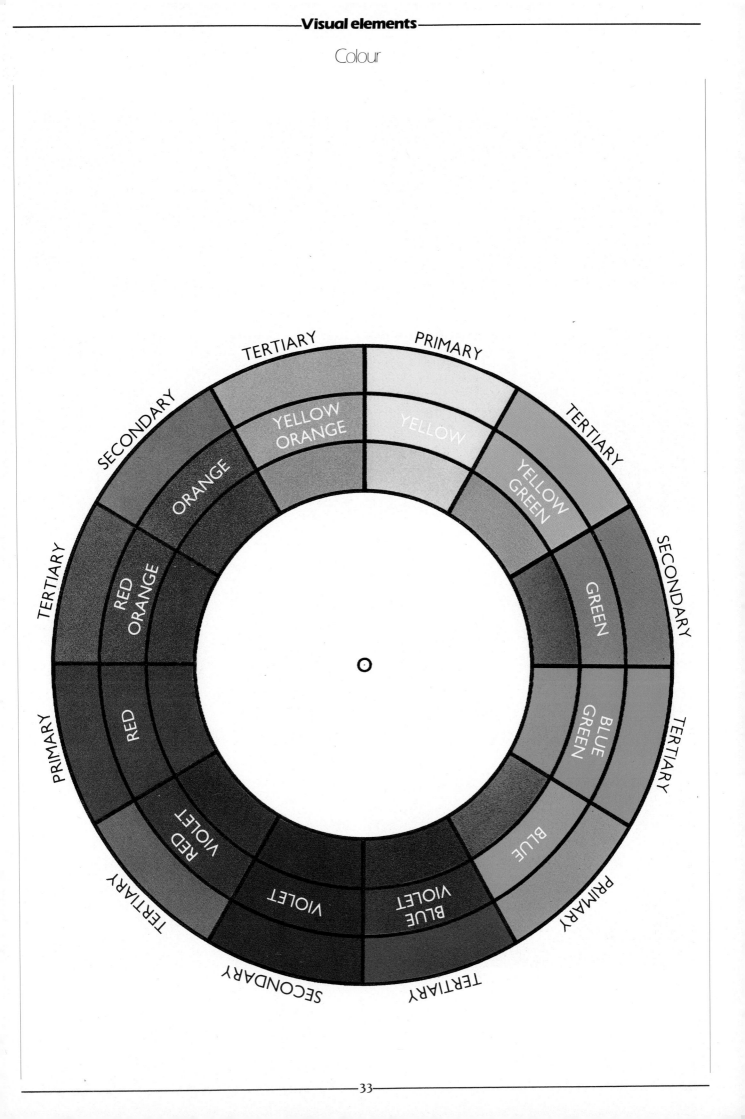

Colour

Words associated with colour

1   Bright

5   Exciting

2   Shocking

6   Subtle

3   Harmonious

7   Camouflaged

4   Attractive

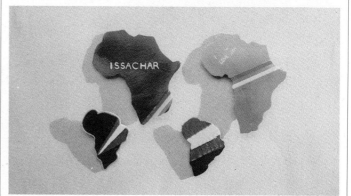

8   Identifying

1 Flower stall	5 Indian fabric stall
2 Painted face	6 Sea urchins
3 Acrylic camel	7 Caterpillar
4 Flower attracting bee	8 Rastafarian badges

Colour

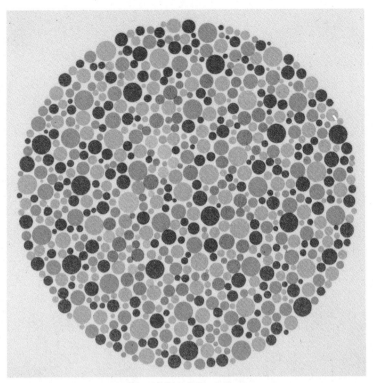

Colour blindness chart

School projects

Dyed laminated shavings

Kung fu fighters

Leather belt and punch

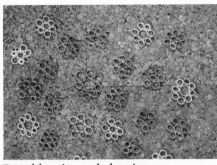

Stylized animals

Gnome jigsaws

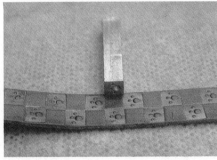

Acrylic feelies

Resin windows

Wooden vehicles

Tin-plate sculptures

Colour

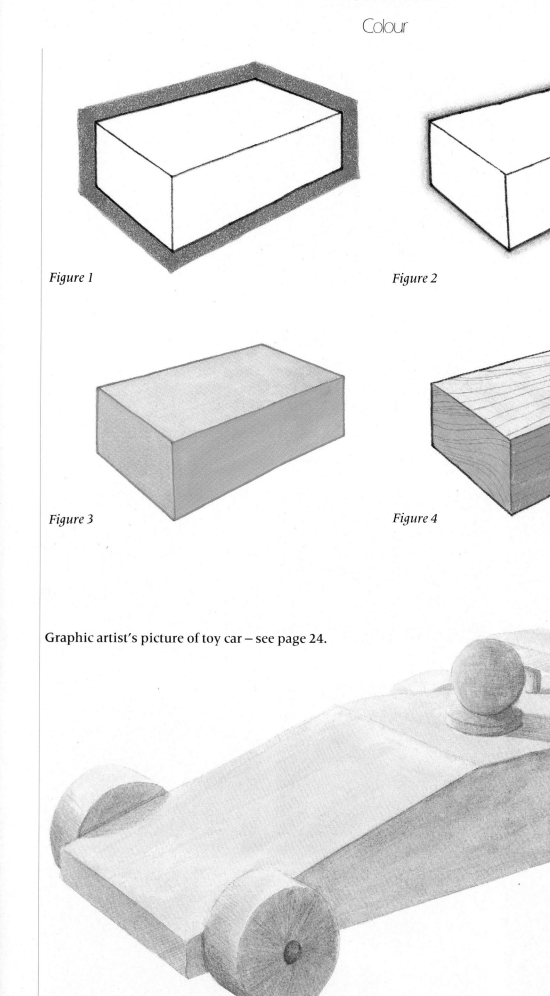

Figure 1

Figure 2

Figure 3

Figure 4

Graphic artist's picture of toy car – see page 24.

Combining the elements

We have seen that visual design has various elements. We have looked at line, shape and form, texture, and colour.

We can now look at the way designers put these elements together. There are certain principles of design. They include balance, proportion, harmony, contrast, pattern, movement, rhythm, and style.

As you look at these principles, remember that they are only a guide. We cannot say that a design is 'right' or 'wrong'. It depends on what the designer wanted. When *you* design something, *you* must take the design decisions.

FASHION DESIGNER.

PATTERN

TOWN PLANNER.

HARMONY + CONTRAST

JEWELLERY DESIGNER.

STYLE

ARCHITECT.

MOVEMENT + RHYTHM

FURNITURE DESIGNER.

BALANCE + PROPORTION

Balance

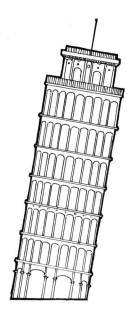

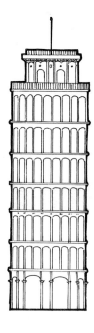

If you walk along the top of a wall, you need to keep your balance. You may keep your balance by holding out your arms. The weight on one side of you matches the weight on the other.

As designers we need to be aware of visual balance. Our brains are conditioned to accept pictures and objects that look balanced. Our brains also reject objects which are not balanced. For instance, would the Leaning Tower of Pisa be so famous if it was vertical?

Designers think about three sorts of balance. The first sort is **symmetrical balance**. Imagine a line drawn down the middle of an object. The object is symmetrical if one half is a mirror-image of the other half. Look at these examples.

Using symmetry is an easy way of providing balance. Some designers think it is unexciting, or too safe. They prefer other sorts of balance.

The objects in the pictures below are not symmetrical. But the left-hand side and the right-hand side still balance visually. They have **asymmetric balance**.

The third type of balance is **radial balance**. The balance radiates outward from a point somewhere near the middle. The pattern may be circular or spiral. Many natural objects have this kind of balance.

Butterfly

Sea horse

Nautilus shell

Seat

Pierced pendant

Daisy

Syon House

Swan

Cactus

Proportion

Different parts of an object are related to each other in size. For instance, one part may be twice as long as another. Similarly one object may be three times as tall as another object. This relationship is called **proportion**.

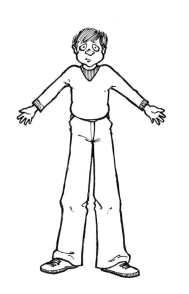

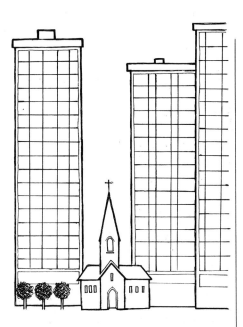

Proportion can seem right or wrong. In the examples above, the proportions seem wrong.

For many centuries people have envied nature's ability to create good proportions. People have tried to find mathematical formulae for these proportions. The Greeks felt that they had solved the problem with the **golden mean**. This is a mathematical formula that produces a rectangle of 'pleasing' proportions. It is based on the two sides of the rectangle being in the ratio of 1 to 1·618.

You can draw a rectangle using the golden mean.

★ *Draw a base line.*
★ *Draw a square. The length of the side of the square is the length of the short side of the rectangle.*
★ *Measure halfway along the base of the square (Figure 1). Put the point of your compasses here. Now draw an arc from the top corner of the square to the base line.*
★ *The point where the arc touches the base line is the corner of the rectangle. Draw a vertical line upwards from it. Then extend the top of the square to complete the rectangle.*

The Greeks used this ratio in a lot of their designs. The most famous example is a building called the Parthenon, in Athens.

There was a mathematician called Leonardo Fibonacci. He lived in Italy, probably from 1170 to 1250. He investigated a series of numbers now called the **Fibonacci series**. It starts like this: 0,1,1,2,3,5,8,13,21,34,55. You can make the series longer. Each number is the sum of the previous two numbers. So 3 + 5 is 8, and 5 + 8 is 13.

There is a curious thing about the Fibonacci series. If you divide one number in it by the next smaller number the answer is roughly 1.618!

It is strange that numbers in the Fibonacci series keep occurring in nature. Measure the distance from the top of your head to your navel. Then measure the distance from your navel to the ground. Divide the larger number by the smaller number. What answer do you get?

Good proportion in design has to be decided by eye. You cannot just use formulae. And your eyes can play tricks. Look at the lines in Figure 2. Which one is longer? Do the same with Figure 3. Use a ruler to measure the lines. Were you right?

In design, answers are not 'right' or 'wrong'. You have to look at them and decide for yourself.

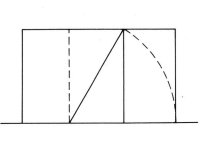

Figure 1

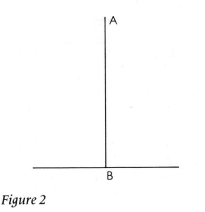

Figure 2

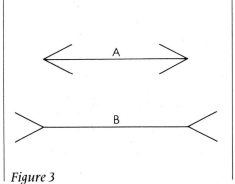

Figure 3

Harmony and contrast

When you listen to a group of singers, you hear many different sounds. Often you hear several sounds at the same moment. They may sound good together. This is called **harmony**. Or they may sound harsh together. This is discord or **contrast**.

People who compose music usually want it to sound harmonious. But they may want to attract your attention, or to surprise you. Then they deliberately make contrasts. Contrasts may make you feel excited, or angry, or wide awake.

Designers use harmony and contrast in the same way. You usually want to make your work attractive. You want to please other people. You want them to feel comfortable with your work. But sometimes you may want to catch people's attention, so you may use contrast.

This is a wooden sculpture. It is harmonious. The designer thought about these points.

* *The shape of the frame uses the golden mean.*
* *The smaller rectangles are not all the same size.*
* *The units in the rectangles have different shapes. They are interesting shapes.*
* *The units have different colours, and different textures.*
* *The grain in the wood fits with the form of the whole sculpture.*
* *The units have positive shapes. The spaces between them are negative shapes. These negative shapes are also interesting.*

The wooden sculpture is harmonious. So is the metal window pendant. But they are not just symmetrical. One part of the design balances another part.

Look at the window pendant. The flowers at the bottom left are quite unlike the rest of the pendant. They provide a contrast. You can make contrast in lots of ways. You can contrast thick heavy lines with fine delicate ones. You can contrast geometric shapes with organic ones. You can contrast rough textures with smooth textures. You can contrast warm colours with cool ones.

Contrast comes from mixing things that are different. If they look good together, you have harmony. If they clash, you have contrast.

Pattern

Pattern is one of the most interesting and challenging principles of visual design. Everywhere we look we can see patterns. Patterns may be planned, random, structural, accidental, natural or they may be designed to conceal.

Most of the patterns that we see are carefully planned. Sometimes they make a plain surface more interesting. At other times the patterns may fulfil some special purpose. For example, the patterns on the giraffe and zebra are used for **camouflage**.

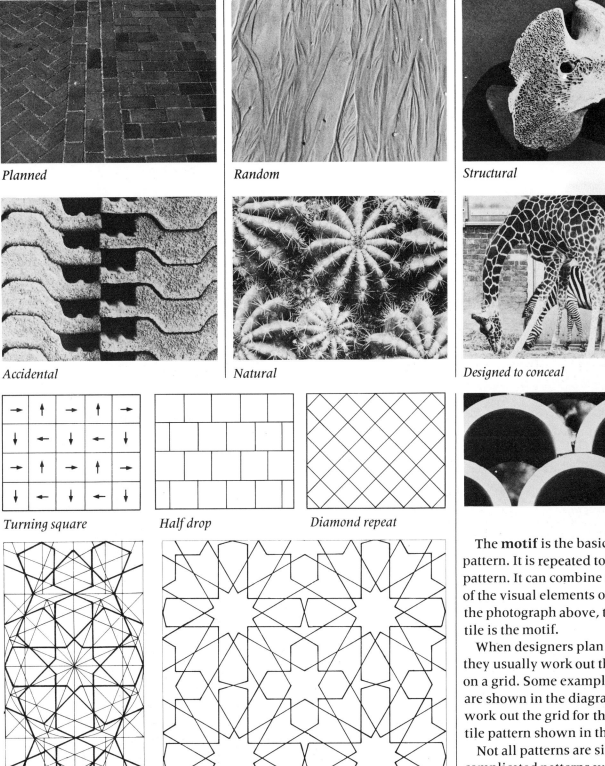

Planned

Random

Structural

Accidental

Natural

Designed to conceal

Turning square

Half drop

Diamond repeat

The **motif** is the basic part of a pattern. It is repeated to make the pattern. It can combine any or all of the visual elements of design. In the photograph above, the curved tile is the motif.

When designers plan a pattern they usually work out the pattern on a grid. Some examples of grids are shown in the diagrams. Try to work out the grid for the curved tile pattern shown in the photo.

Not all patterns are simple. These complicated patterns were designed by Islamic people.

Movement and rhythm

Some music contains clear tunes. The tunes seem to wander, run or dance. They have **movement**. Often the music has a strong **rhythm**. You may tap your feet in time with the rhythm.

Designs can have movement and rhythm as well. Your ears hear movement and rhythm in music. And your eyes may see movement and rhythm in objects. As a designer, you can use movement and rhythm in your designs.

Look at the designs below. The staircase and the tree are both spiralling. They have a feeling of movement. The tree pendant has lots of lines. These suggest movement in the branches. The bowl has colour, shape and line. They all give rhythm to the bowl.

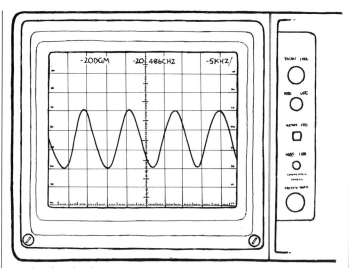

Notice the rhythm of the line shown up on the oscilloscope

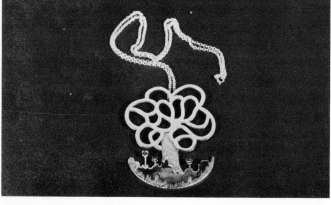

Style

There are *elements* of visual design. These are line, shape and form, texture, and colour. There are also *principles* of visual design. We have looked at balance, proportion, harmony and contrast, pattern, and movement and rhythm. You will use all these when you design something.

You can design an article any way you like. There is no need to design things the way other people design them. You can often tell who designed something, just by looking at it. For example, the paintings by Claude Monet are all different. But they have the same flavour, so you can tell they are by Monet. Monet has a **style** you can recognize. Monet's paintings aren't exact copies, like photographs.

They are just impressions. Other French painters liked Monet's style. For instance, Renoir, Pissaro and Sisley started to paint like Monet. Their style of painting was called **impressionism.** Impressionism became popular. Some composers, such as Debussy, wrote music in the same style.

Style depends on all sorts of things. It depends on the materials available and how much they cost. It depends on the country. It depends on the knowledge of the designer. It depends on technology.

Style also depends on fashion. Look at these lamps. They show six different styles. Each style was in fashion for a while. How did people live at these times? Does

this tell you anything about why the styles were fashionable?

You will design things. You will develop your own style. Here are three points to think about.

★ *You now know the elements and principles of visual design. Do not think of them as separate. They are all related. They are all important for each article you make.*

★ *You will now notice designs more than you did before. Think about the elements and principles. Think about how they relate. The more you design, the more you notice about other people's designs.*

★ *When you design things, try to make sure that as well as working they also look good.*

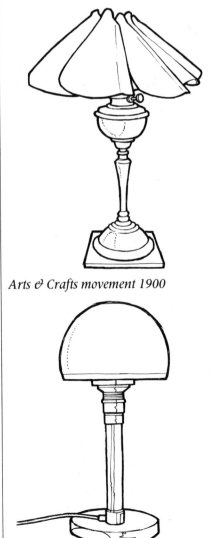

Arts & Crafts movement 1900

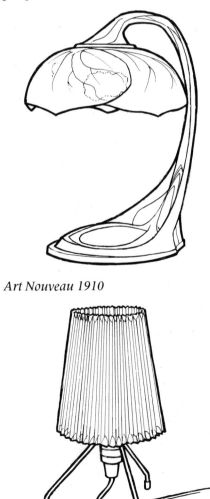

Art Nouveau 1910

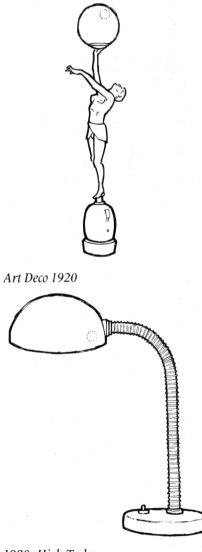

Art Deco 1920

Bauhaus 1930

1950s

1980s High Tech

Design in nature

Nature is a wonderful designer. Look at the plants and animals near you. Take a magnifying glass – it will show you more detail.

Animals need to move. They need to keep warm. And they need to eat food. Plants need to stand straight, even in the wind and rain. Animals and plants need to survive. Think how their design helps them to do this.

When you look at animals and plants, think about the visual elements and the technological principles of design. What can you see? How are the elements and principles combined?

The photographs on these pages were taken during one visit to a London park. They show many of the problems faced by human designers. Study an area near you in the same way – it doesn't matter where it is. Draw or photograph things you see. You may be surprised by what you find!

Figure 1

Figure 2

Figure 3

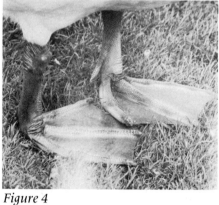

Figure 4

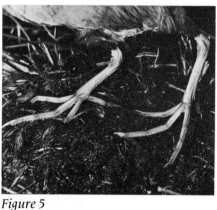

Figure 5

Figure 6

★ *Figure 1 shows new leaves on a large plant. Notice the spikes. These protect the plant.*

★ *Figure 2 shows a bee. The bee collects pollen from flowers. It stores the pollen in two little sacks on its legs.*

★ *Figure 3 shows an earthworm. How does it tunnel through the earth?*

★ *Figure 4 shows the feet of a swan. The feet are used for swimming.*

★ *Figure 5 shows the feet of a moorhen. These feet are used for scratching the ground.*

★ *Figure 6 shows a spider's web. Notice the lines that show its structure.*

Design in nature

Figure 7

Figure 8

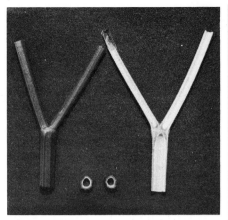

Figure 9

Figure 10

Figure 11

Figure 12

★ *Figure 7 shows a spider. This is one of nature's designers!*
★ *Figure 8 shows a plant. Can you find numbers in the Fibonacci series?*
★ *Figure 9 shows parts of the same plant. Examine the structure of the stem. How does the structure help the plant to stand up?*

★ *Figure 10 shows a climbing plant. It clings to other things for support. How does it do this?*
★ *Figure 11 shows a snail. The snail carries its home with it. Notice the pattern of the shell.*
★ *Figure 12 shows a woodlouse. It has a suit of armour that allows it to roll up into a protected ball.*

Using technology

Technology is the application of scientific knowledge to the solution of human problems. The problem may be to improve the environment. It may be to provide amusement. Or it may be to make life easier. Technology is a vast subject. It links together many aspects of our lives.

Humans are now the dominant animals on Earth. This is because they can develop and use technology. All civilizations have similar needs. People needed food, so they invented ploughs and hoes, spears and guns. People needed transport, so they tamed oxen and horses, and invented boats and wheels. People needed shelter, so they made clothes and buildings. People found ways of controlling things and collecting energy. They developed materials and methods of working with them. Technology has grown rapidly.

Technology can be used for good or bad reasons. Sometimes good intentions have disastrous results. For example, many American plains were ploughed. Then there were no plants to hold the soil in place. The result was a large dust bowl.

Technology can provide great benefits. But it also carries great responsibility. You must think about the environmental and social effects of technology. When you design something, you must consider how it looks and how it will fit into your environment.

Technology is especially useful in these three ways.

★ *You can control things you've made.*
★ *You can use and develop energy resources.*
★ *You can learn more about materials and how to use them.*

These three aspects of technology are related to each other. And they are also related to the processes of designing and making articles.

You will be doing projects, so you will be designing and making articles. This section of the book gives you a lot of useful information. You will learn about structures, electronics, mechanisms, energy, and materials. In each case, there will be information and examples of use. But it is up to you to decide what to use in your own projects. You will have to think about what each article requires. Then you can choose the best material, the best structure, the best source of energy and so on. You will have to think about whether they are available, and what they cost.

At the start of your work as a designer, your measurements will not need to be exact. But you will need to be more and more accurate as you make more complicated projects. So it is a good idea to be as accurate as you can right from the start.

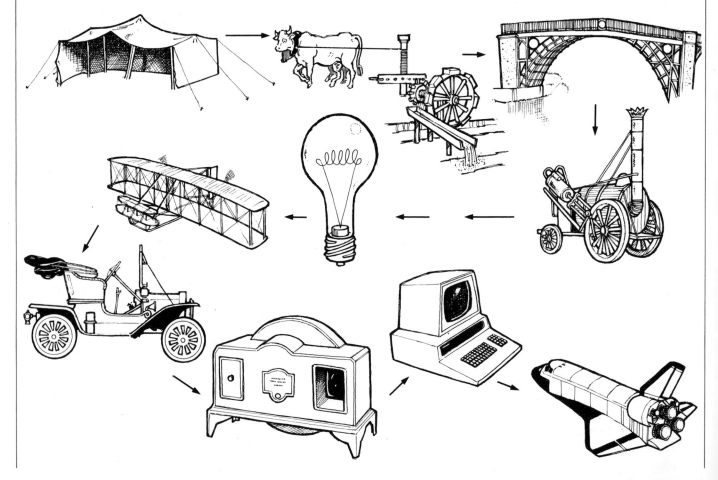

Using technology

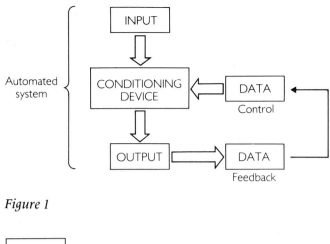

Figure 1

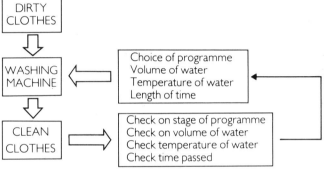

Figure 2

Useful terms in technology

Technology develops all the time. There are lots of new words to describe ideas in technology. Here are just a few that you may find useful.

Automation   The process of making machines do a piece of work, instead of people. For example, peas were once shelled by hand. Now they can be shelled by machine. So pea shelling has been automated.

Conditioning device   A machine that turns one kind of input into another kind of output. For example, a light meter turns the amount of light that reaches it into a movement of a pointer.

Control   The process of measuring some part of a situation, and then making it the way you want it. For example, the thermostat in a central heating system measures the temperature of a room and then turns on more heat if necessary.

Data   Information used for working. For example, the measurements for a design are data.

Feedback   The process of checking the result of a change, and making further changes if necessary. For example, the water level in a river may be controlled by a sluice gate. If the water level above the gate is too high, the gate is opened. As the water flows away, information about the level is fed back to the controlling unit. The gate is closed again when the water is at the level required.

Input   What goes into something. It may be energy, force or information. For example, the electricity used by a light bulb is input energy.

Output   What comes out of something. It may also be energy, force or information. For example, the light that comes out of a light bulb is output energy.

System   An organized means of working. You can arrange conditioning devices, control mechanisms, input, output and feedback of data in many ways to make different systems. Figure 1 shows just one arrangement. Figure 2 shows an example of this system.

Structures

A **structure** provides support. The support must not be able to collapse. Nature and man have constructed many kinds of structure. Many animals have skeletons to support them. Plants may have something similar. Other structures provide shelter and transport.

A structure must be able to resist **forces.** Its appearance and cost are less important. If a structure cannot resist the forces that act on it, it will collapse. It will then be worthless.

There are two types of force – external and internal. To keep the form of an object, the internal forces must exactly match the external forces (*Figure 1*).

External forces may be static or dynamic. **Static forces** are stationary (*Figure 2*). They are caused by the structure itself. For example, a television standing on a table exerts a force on that table. **Dynamic forces** are moving (*Figure 3*). They are caused by something acting on the structure. For example, wind, waves,

vehicles and people can all cause dynamic forces. Dynamic forces can change rapidly. They are the most common reason for structural failures.

Suppose you are designing a simple project. The structure of your design may be vital to the success of the project. Look at the piece of wood on page 83 (*Figure 9*). This will break easily, because of the direction of the grain. When you design structures, you must think about two important questions:

★ *What will happen to the structure when external force is applied?*
★ *How should the material be used most effectively? (For example, which way should the grain run in a wooden structure?)*

Material must be able to support a **load.** However, material is not always better for this job just because it is thicker and heavier.

Structures from Nature

Man-made structures

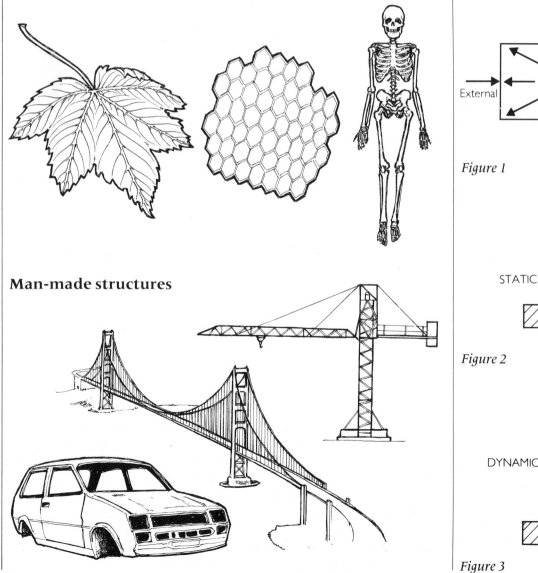

Figure 1

Figure 2

Figure 3

Forces

Various different kinds of force can act on a structure. Several forces may act at the same time.

Material may be pulled. The pulling force is called **tension** (*Figure 4*). For example, imagine a rope pulling a car. The rope is under tension. It has a *tensile* load upon it.

Material may be pressed. The pressing force is called **compression** (*Figure 5*). For example, the wheel of a lorry on the road is under compression. The road has a *compressive* load upon it.

Material may be pressed from both sides. This kind of pressing force is called **shear** (*Figure 6*). For example, when you cut a piece of paper with scissors, the paper is under shear. It has a **shearing** load upon it.

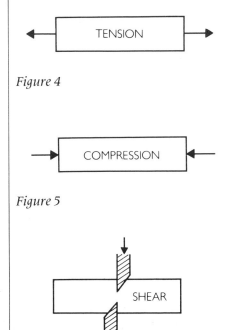

TENSION

Figure 4

COMPRESSION

Figure 5

SHEAR

Figure 6

Triangulation

Structures are made of individual parts called **members**. The members are under tension or compression. Shear forces normally occur where members are joined. A member in tension is called a **tie**. A member under compression is called a **strut**.

Look at the examples in Figure 7. You can see that *ties* may be made of string or rope, but *struts* must be rigid.

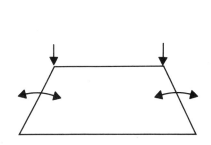

Ties

Strut

TELEPHONE POLE

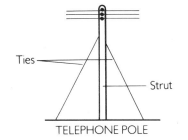

Tie

Strut

HANGING SIGN

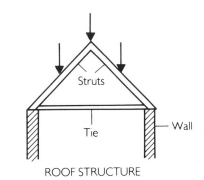

Struts

Tie

Wall

ROOF STRUCTURE

Figure 7

Notice that the structures above are all triangular. You can build many stable structures by **triangulation**. Look at the roof structure. If the tie was removed, the roof would drop. It would push the walls outwards. The simple structure in Figure 8 shows the value of triangulation.

This structure will fold easily.

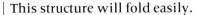

Figure 8(a)

The member marked *A* is rigid. The whole structure is rigid.

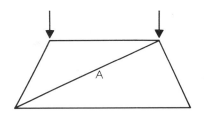

A

Figure 8(b)

The member marked *B* is unnecessary. It is **redundant.**

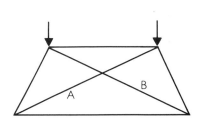

A

B

Figure 8(c)

When you design something, think about the structure. It must be strong. This may depend on how it is used. For example, roll a piece of paper into a cylinder. If you place a small book on the side, the cylinder will flatten immediately. But if you put the book on the end, the cylinder will support it.

Beams

When a **beam** supports a load, the beam may bend. For instance, a shelf will bend when loaded in the centre (*Figure 1*). The load compresses the top surface. As the beam bends, the lower surface is stretched (*Figure 2*). The top surface of the beam must resist compression. The bottom surface must resist tension. The centre of the beam need not be very strong, but it keeps the outside surface rigid.

One special kind of beam is called a **cantilever** (*Figure 3*). It is supported at one end only. In this beam, the *top* surface is in tension and the *bottom* surface is in compression.

Application 1 What is the lightest beam that is 50 mm wide, spans 400 mm and can carry 5 kg weight? You may use card, paper, wood, string, or any other suitable material. Look at other beams around you. They may help you to solve this problem. Think about the principles explained above.

Beams can have many different shapes. Look at Figure 4.

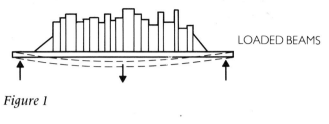
LOADED BEAMS

Figure 1

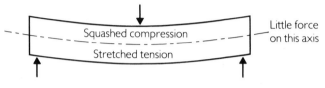

Figure 2

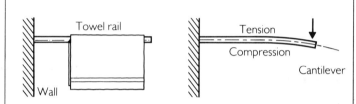

Figure 3

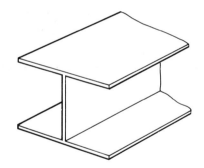
I-section

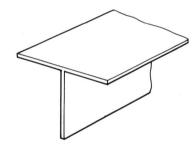
T-section

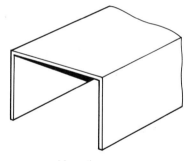
U-section

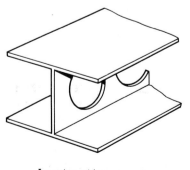
I-section with less weight in centre

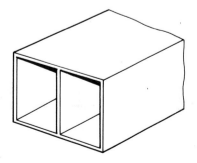
Box-section, this may have an internal member

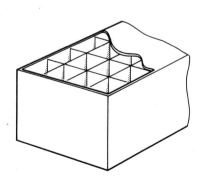
This structure uses the strength of the material

Figure 4

Application 2   Suppose you need a structure to support a weight of 10 kg, 500 mm above a work surface. The structure must be rigid, but as light as possible.

You could use a range of materials. An open framework may be a good solution. Look at the diagrams.

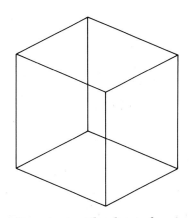

You start with a basic frame.

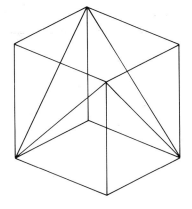

You could use simple cross members to triangulate this frame.

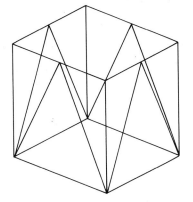

Or you could use more material, like this. The triangles carry some of the weight.

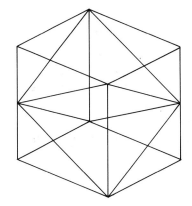

You could also trianglulate the frame like this. This structure is more rigid.

Application 3   Suppose you want a box to hold four identical delicate objects. The objects might be eggs, or Christmas tree decorations.

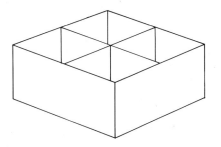

This is the simplest design. The box is not very rigid.

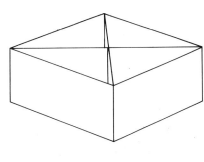

This box is rigid. But it wastes space. It may be uneconomic.

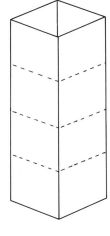

This box is rigid, compact and economical.

You need to consider the support materials when you are designing a structure. Corrugated card is very good for structures like the box above. Many industries pack delicate objects in expanded polystyrene containers. These are light and can withstand knocks.

Electronics

A lot of machines are driven by **electricity**. In your home, for example, you may have a clock, a washing machine, a shaver, a refrigerator, a vacuum cleaner and a television all using electricity.

Electricity is provided by the movement of electrons. The rate of movement is called the **current**. Current is measured in **amperes**, or **amps** (A). The electrons are moved by a force called the **electron-moving force,** or **emf.** Emf is measured in **volts** (V). In Britain, the mains supply has a force of about 240 volts. In Europe, the mains supply is about 120 volts.

The electrons usually move along wires. Some materials allow electrons to move through them easily: these materials are **conductors.** Metals such as copper and iron are good conductors. Other materials do not allow electrons to move through them easily: these materials are **insulators.** Plastic and rubber are good insulators. Materials that are good insulators have high **resistance.** Materials that are good conductors have low resistance. Resistance is measured in **ohms** (Ω).

You can make a bulb light up by connecting it with wires to a battery (*Figure 1*). The battery provides the emf. The wires conduct the electricity. The system forms a complete ring, and is known as an **electrical circuit.** If the circuit is not complete, it is called a **broken circuit.** Faulty connections may make a **short circuit.** Here electrons flow round a path other than the one intended. The amount of current that flows (I) depends on the electrical force (V) and the resistance in the circuit (R).

$$\text{Current} = \frac{\text{force}}{\text{resistance}}$$

This formula can be rearranged to this form:

$$\text{Force} = \text{current} \times \text{resistance}$$

This is represented as $V = I \times R$.

We now know a lot about the movement of electrons in circuits, and how to control them. This subject is called **electronics.** You can use electrons to detect, to measure, to control, to indicate and to provide power. Most of this is done by a combination of simple switches and resistors. **Switches** connect or disconnect circuits. **Resistors** control the amount of current flowing in circuits.

Suppose you are designing an electrical circuit . You are likely to discover that part of it needs to be complicated electronics. You can show this part of the main circuit by drawing a box. You don't need to worry about how the box will work. Just write down what the box needs to do (*Figure 2*). Then you can design the contents of the box later, or get someone else to do it for you. This is called **black box design.** You will need a lot of practice before you can design all your own circuits!

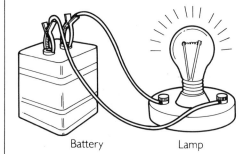
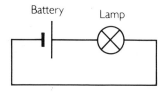

Battery Lamp Circuit diagram

Figure 1

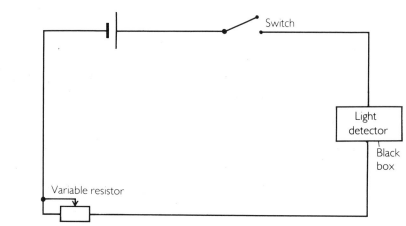

Figure 2

Resistors

Resistors are electronic components that let you control the current in a circuit.

Fixed resistors have a constant amount of resistance (*Figure 3*). For example, you might have a 10 Ω resistor, or a 4600 Ω resistor. The resistance is shown by coloured bands round the resistor (*Figure 4*).

Colour	First band	Second band	Third band
Black	0	0	Ω
Brown	1	1	0 Ω
Red	2	2	00 Ω
Orange	3	3	000 Ω
Yellow	4	4	0000 Ω
Green	5	5	00000 Ω
Blue	6	6	000000 Ω
Violet	7	7	
Grey	8	8	
White	9	9	

These are read in order along the resistor. A resistor coloured orange–blue–red has a resistance of 3600 Ω. The word 'kilo' is used for 'thousand', and shown as **k**. 3600 Ω is the same as 3.6 kΩ.

   Resistors have a fourth band separate from the others. This fourth band is usually silver or gold. It indicates how accurately the resistance has been measured. This accuracy is called **tolerance**.

Variable resistors can be set to different amounts of resistance, as required (*Figure 5*). You may find a dial attached to a variable resistor. This dial lets you choose the resistance you want.

Light dependent resistors or **photocells** change resistance with light (*Figure 6*). When the photocell is well lit, it has a low resistance. When the photocell is dark, it has a high resistance.

Temperature–dependent resistors, or **thermistors** change resistance with temperature (*Figure 7*). When the thermistor is hot, it has a low resistance. When it is cold, it has a high resistance.

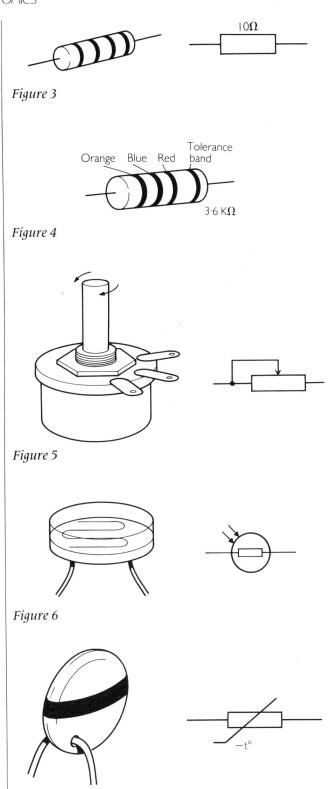

Figure 3

Figure 4

Figure 5

Figure 6

Figure 7

Further components

Here are some more useful electronic components. Each is shown in two ways. One way is the way the component looks. The other is a symbol used in circuit diagrams.

Diodes allow current to flow in one direction only (*Figure 1*).

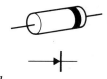

Figure 1

Electrolytic capacitors store electricity (*Figure 2*).

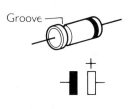

Figure 2

Transistors are fast switches (*Figure 3*).

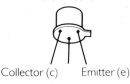

Figure 3

Loadspeakers change electrical energy into sound energy (*Figure 4*).

Figure 4

Motors change electrical energy into kinetic energy (*Figure 5*).

Figure 5

Wires connect components together (*Figure 6*).

Plain wire

Wires connected

Wires that cross but are not connected

Figure 6

Building circuits

You can build circuits in three stages.
* *Model the circuit with a quick assembly kit.*
* *Build the circuit with individual components, so you can test the circuit and make simple adjustments if necessary.*
* *Build the permanent circuit for use.*

Modelling the circuit
This is an easy way to try out your design. The components are in boxes. Boxes are placed together to form the circuit.

Your school may or may not have this kind of modelling system. One common system is the Locktronics system (*Figure 7*). Such systems are useful, but too expensive for permanent use.

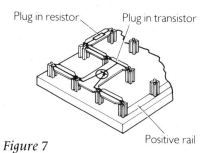

Plug in resistor   Plug in transistor

Positive rail

Figure 7

Building with reusable components
This is a useful way to experiment with circuits, because the components can be taken apart and used again. It is fairly cheap. But circuits made like this are usually too big and untidy for permanent use. Your school may have a system such as the ones shown below.

S-Dec This uses a plastic board with metal clips beneath (*Figure 8*). Components are pushed into holes. If the Dec has been used many times, it may not provide good connections.

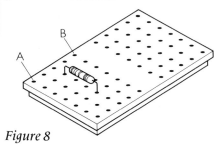

Figure 8

Dobbs or BBC Board This uses a piece of softwood or soft board. Connections are made with screws and screwcups, so you can see the connections in the circuit (*Figure 9*). The system is cheap, but rather untidy. Vibration may loosen the components.

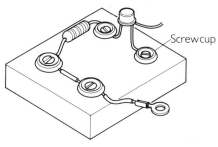

Screwcup

Figure 9

You can improve the system by fitting small tension springs to the board. (*Figure 10*). These make it easier and quicker to connect components. But vibration may still cause breaks in the circuit.

Tension spring screwed to base board

Connected through spring pressure

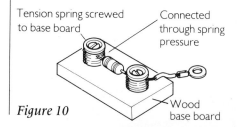

Wood base board

Figure 10

Building permanent circuits

Before building the permanent circuit for your project, you should have tested it. You can now build the final version. The circuit must be robust, and reliable. There are several ways of doing this.

Etched printed circuit boards (pcb)

This is a simple method of making individual printed circuits. It is unlikely that short circuits will occur.

First you need some copper laminated board. You draw your circuit on this, using an **etch-resistant pen** or **rubdown transfers** *(Figure 11)*. (Notice that this will be the mirror image of the circuit diagram as you look at the copper side of the pcb. This is because the components are placed on the plastic side of the laminate.) You leave out the components. Next you remove the copper, except where the circuit is marked. You do this by putting the board in an etching liquid such as ferric chloride. **Be careful: etching liquid is harmful.** Etching time

depends on the concentration of the etching liquid. For example, 500 g ferric chloride in 1 litre water gives an etching time of 15–20 minutes.

Carefully take the board from the etching liquid. Wash the board thoroughly. Scour the remaining copper to get rid of the etch-resistant material *(Figure 12)*. The circuit is now ready. But to make it last longer, you should protect it with a coat of lacquer. (You can make jewellery by the same process.)

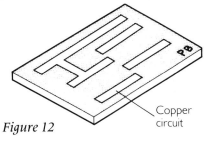

Figure 12

Now fit the components. You need to drill a small hole where each component will be. Then fit the component through the hole and solder it *(Figure 13)*. See page 89.

Matrix boards   These are plastic laminated boards with a series of holes. You build circuits by pushing pins into the board. You then attach the components to the parts of the pins that stick out of the board *(Figure 14)*. Matrix boards are less attractive and less effective than pcbs. But they are useful if you have no etching facilities.

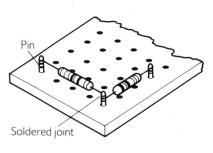

Figure 14

Stripboards   These are similar to matrix boards, but connections are provided by copper laminate *(Figure 15)*. Connections are in one direction only. Stripboard is expensive and less effective than pcb's.

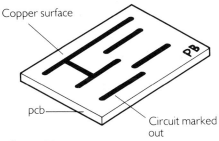

Figure 11

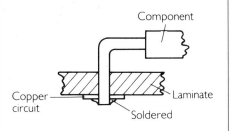

Figure 13

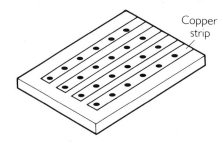

Figure 15

Switches

On page 52 there is a picture of a light bulb connected to a battery. When the battery and the bulb are linked to make a complete circuit, current flows and the bulb lights up. But you do not want the bulb lit all the time, you need a **switch** to turn it on and off (*Figure 1*).

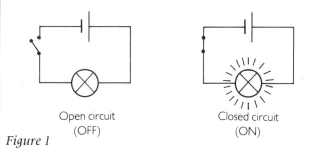

Open circuit
(OFF)

Closed circuit
(ON)

Figure 1

There are lots of different kinds of switch. Figure 2 shows five kinds – a **toggle** switch, a **slide** switch, a **rotary** switch, a **rocker** switch and a **press-button** switch. You can decide which one is best for your own project.

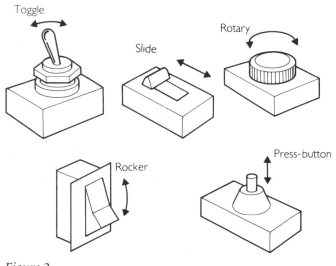

Toggle

Slide

Rotary

Rocker

Press-button

Figure 2

Switches can be used to make several interesting small projects. For example, you can make games. Use a dry battery for any game you make – **never use the mains!** One of the best known games is a test of how steady your hand is. You have to move a loop along a bent piece of wire without touching the wire (*Figure 3*). If you touch the wire, you complete a circuit and a bell rings. So *you* are acting as a switch.

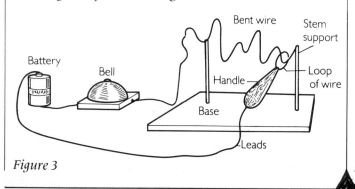

Bent wire

Stem support

Battery

Bell

Handle

Loop of wire

Base

Leads

Figure 3

Applications Sometimes you need to make your own switch. One good way is to use a piece of bent copper strip (*Figure 4*). To close the switch, you press on the piece sticking up.

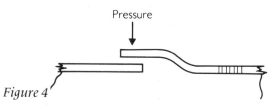

Pressure

Figure 4

A switch works by closing the gap in a circuit. There is no need for the bit that closes the gap to be joined on to the circuit. Another game is shown in Figure 5. The base of the game is a block of wood with metal on the top. The metal is in two parts, with a gap between. You can make it by etching, or using copper, or tinplate, or aluminium foil. The block can be any shape. You connect a battery to a bulb and to each part of the base. Now you need a small metal block, with the shorter measurement a bit smaller than the gap. Try to move the block round the gap without touching *both* sides at the same time. If you touch both, you complete the circuit and the bulb lights. A bell may be used instead of the bulb.

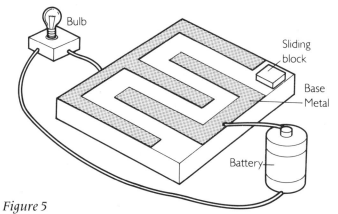

Bulb

Sliding block

Base Metal

Battery

Figure 5

Figure 6 shows another game. In this, you have to roll a metal ball bearing over the surface. If the ball bearing falls into the groove, it completes the circuit. Design some more games using switches. You will have to think carefully about how they work.

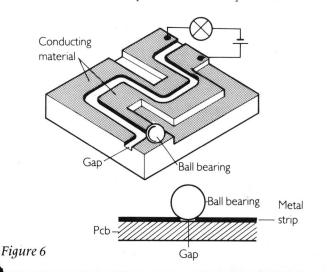

Conducting material

Gap

Ball bearing

Ball bearing

Metal strip

Pcb

Gap

Figure 6

When you have made the game, make a box to keep it in. Figure 7 gives one idea.

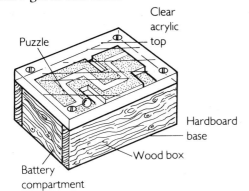

Figure 7

You can make more complicated games that use several switches. You could make one in which you have to get ball bearings in four holes before a bulb will light (*Figure 8*). In this case the circuit has four switches. They must *all* be closed for the bulb to light. So the switches must be placed **in series** (*Figure 9*). Or you could make it so that the bulb lights if *any one* of the bearings is in a hole. Then the switches must be **in parallel** (*Figure 10*).

A switch can control two circuits at once. Figure 11 shows a circuit with two lamps. One or other of the lamps is always on. You could make these into a pair of illuminated signs.

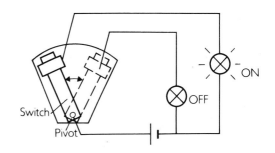

Figure 11

You can use a similar pivoted switch to change the direction of a motor (*Figure 12*). You could use this motor to drive a small conveyor belt.

Other electronic components of a circuit can be placed in series or in parallel. Make a circuit with a battery and a lamp (*Figure 13*). Note the brightness of the lamp. Now add a second, identical lamp (*Figure 14*). You will see that the lamps are now dimmer. This is because each lamp has resistance, so less current flows. The bigger the resistance, the less the current. So you can control the brightness of a lamp by putting a variable resistor in the circuit (*Figure 15*). Now you can use the variable resistor as a **dimmer switch**. When you change the resistance, you change the brightness of the light. You can control the speed of a motor in the same way.

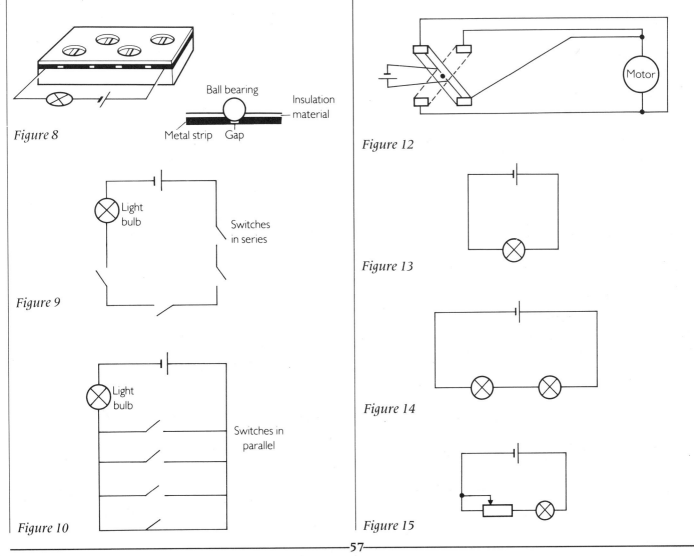

Figure 8

Figure 9

Figure 10

Figure 12

Figure 13

Figure 14

Figure 15

Sensing devices

It is very useful to have devices that are sensitive to the conditions around them. These devices operate because of a change in resistance. More or less current flows depending on the conditions.

Some of these devices were mentioned on page 53. Suppose you have a circuit with a lamp, a battery and a light-dependent resistor (*Figure 1*). When it is *dark*, the resistor has high resistance. Not much current flows, so the lamp is *dim*. When conditions are *brighter*, the resistance is less. More current flows, and the lamp shines *brightly*.

A thermistor is similar, but depends on temperature (*Figure 2*). When the temperature is *low*, the thermistor has a high resistance and the lamp is *dim*. When the temperature is *higher*, the thermistor has a lower resistance and the lamp is *brighter*.

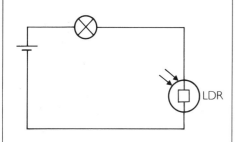

Figure 1

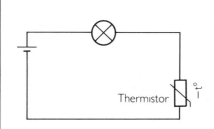

Figure 2

Thermistors and light-dependent resistors are bought as ready-made components. But you can make a simple water sensor. Water conducts electricity. So you can use rain as a switch! Make the sensor with two pieces of wire.

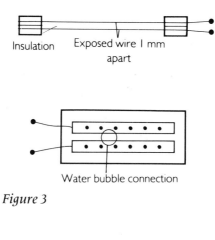

Figure 3

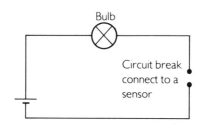

Figure 4

They must be close but not touching (*Figure 3*). Connect them to a battery and a bulb (*Figure 4*). When rain drops on the wires, it completes the circuit and the bell rings.

Transistors

Circuits like the ones shown above are not sensitive. To improve the sensitivity a **transistor** can be introduced into the circuit. The transistor is connected to two sources of current. One current, the **base current**, controls the resistance of the transistor. The other current, the **collector current**, controls the rest of the circuit. The base current is about a hundred times smaller than the collector current. This is why the transistor is so sensitive as a switch. All transistors used in these circuits are n.p.m.

A transistor is shown in Figure 5. When you use one, handle it carefully. Be careful not to overheat it when you solder it. You must not let too much current flow through it. You can protect the transistor by soldering a 1kΩ resistor to the base terminal.

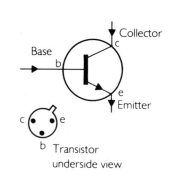

Figure 5

Connect the collector terminal to the *positive* terminal on the battery. Connect the emitter terminal to the *negative* terminal on the battery. A small current flows to the base terminal. When the base current is low, the resistance in the transistor is high. No current flows from collector to emitter. But when the base current is high, the resistance in the transistor is low. More current flows from collector to emitter.

Look at the circuit in Figure 6. The base of the transistor is connected to the *positive* terminal of the battery. There is a base current, so the lamp lights. But in Figure 7 the base is connected to the *negative*

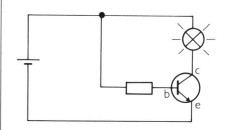

Figure 6

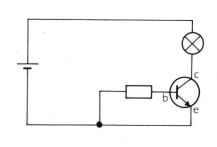

Figure 7

terminal of the battery. There is no base current, so the lamp does not light. You can control the base current by adding a variable resistor (*Figure 8*). If you increase the resistance, you decrease the base current. This increases the resistance of the transistor. Less current flows from collector to emitter. So the lamp becomes dimmer. If you reduce the resistance, the lamp gets brighter.

You can make the device even more sensitive by adding a **potential divider** (*Figure 9*). This uses two resistors. The current at point *P* depends on the ratio of the two resistances. You can make this ratio change if one of the resistors is variable (*Figure 10*). Set the variable resistor to a high resistance. There is high voltage at *P*, so a base current flows to the transistor, and the bulb lights. Set the variable resistor to a low resistance. There is now a low voltage at *P*, so no base current

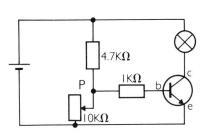

Figure 10

flows to the transistor, and the bulb does not light.

You can use these ideas in the ways shown below.

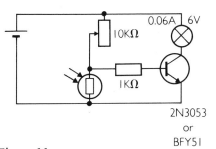

Figure 11

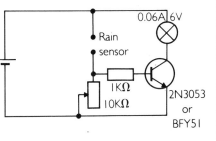

Figure 12

Light sensor (*Figure 11*)   The light-dependent resistor now operates the lamp in the opposite way to that used on page 58. When conditions are dark, the light-dependent resistor has a high resistance. The base current is high, and the lamp lights. The variable resistor controls the light intensity at which the lamp comes on.

Rain sensor (*Figure 12*)   This is like the earlier rain sensor, but more sensitive. The circuit shows a lamp, but a bell or buzzer may be more useful to warn you of the rain.

Temperature sensor   Figure 13 shows a heat-sensing unit. When conditions are hot, the bulb lights. If you exchange the thermistor and the variable resistor, you will have a *cold*-sensing unit. When the conditions are cold, the bulb lights.

Time switch   In this circuit, use a capacitor instead of a sensor. You also need a two-way switch (*Figure 14*). With the switch at *A*, the bulb in the lamp is not lit. Move the switch to *B*. The capacitor begins to charge. When it is charged, the lamp lights. The length of the delay depends on how long the capacitor takes to charge. And this depends on the sizes of the capacitor and the resistance. Capacity is measured in farads (F), or microfarads (μF). There are 1 000 000 μF in 1 F. A 100 μF capacitor gives a delay of about 30 s. A 1000 μF capacitor gives a delay of about 240 s.

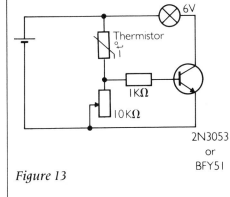

Figure 13

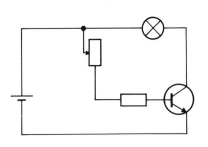

Figure 8

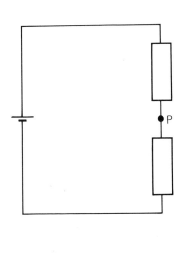

Figure 9

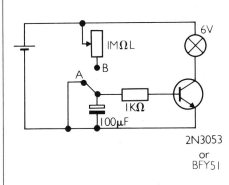

Figure 14

Mechanisms

A **mechanism** is a way of turning one kind of force into another kind of force. One example is a pair of pincers used to remove a nail. The pincers are rotated, and the nail is pulled out (*Figure 1*).

Mechanisms can be combined to form a **machine**. A machine may increase the speed of an operation. Or it may increase the distance travelled. Or it may increase the force that operates. Machines use energy and produce work. Machines can only produce work when energy is supplied. Energy cannot be created. The work produced by a machine cannot be greater than the energy put into the machine. If a machine did exactly the amount of work equivalent to the energy supplied, it would be **100% efficient**. But most machines lose energy as heat or light. They are less than 100% efficient. For example, the engine in a car is only about 30% efficient.

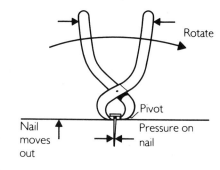

Figure 1

Mechanisms use or create **motion**. There are four basic kinds of motion (*Figure 2*). *Linear* motion is motion in a straight line. *Reciprocating* motion is in a straight line, but backwards and forwards. *Rotary* motion is motion in a circle. *Oscillating* motion is in a circle, but backwards and forwards.

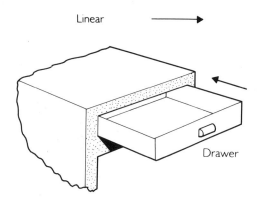

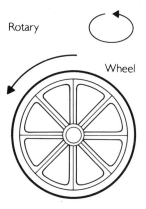

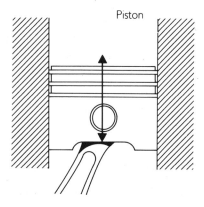

Figure 2

Levers

A rigid beam than can rotate about a fixed point is called a **lever**. The point of rotation is the **fulcrum** or **pivot** (*Figure 3*).

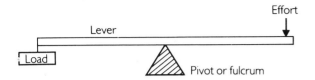

Figure 3

Levers are extremely useful mechanisms. Sometimes a *large input* motion produces a *small output* motion. For instance, you can lever the lid off a tin of paint. A large movement of your hand produces a small movement of the lid (*Figure 4*). But sometimes a *small input* motion produces a *large output* motion. One example is a postal balance. A light envelope produces large movement of the pointer (*Figure 5*).

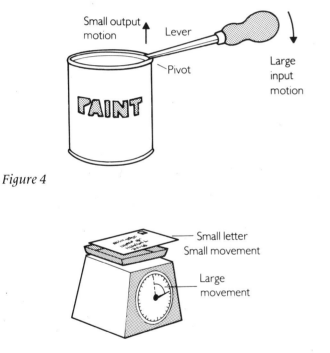

Figure 4

Figure 5

The input force is called the **effort**. The output force is called the **load**. The ratio of effort to load is called the **mechanical advantage**.

$$\text{Mechanical advantage} = \frac{\text{load}}{\text{effort}}$$

Using a lever, you can lift a large load with only a little effort. This may surprise you. Although you use only a small effort, you apply this small effort over a large distance. The large load moves a much smaller distance. The ratio of the distance moved by the effort to the distance moved by the load is called the **velocity ratio.**

$$\text{Velocity ratio} = \frac{\text{distance moved by effort}}{\text{distance moved by load}}$$

There are three kinds of lever. With a **first-class lever**, the pivot is in the middle. The effort is on one side, the load is on the other. With a **second-class lever**, the pivot is at one end. The effort is at the other end, and the load is in the middle. With a **third-class lever**, the pivot is again at one end. But this time the *load* is at the other end, and the *effort* is in the middle. Figure 6 shows examples of these levers.

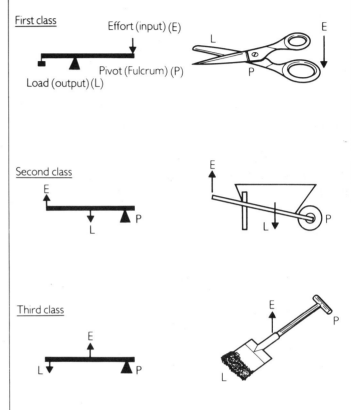

Figure 6

Moments

Imagine a beam with a pivot in the middle. If you press on one side or the other, the beam turns. If the beam is not turning, it must be balanced. It is in **equilibrium.** The forces on one side of the pivot are exactly equal and opposite to the forces on the other side.

The turning force is called a **moment**. The moment depends on the *force*. It also depends on the *distance* of the force from the pivot.

Moment = force × distance of force from pivot

If a beam is in equilibrium, the clockwise moments are equal to the anticlockwise moments (*Figure 7*).

$$3 \times 40 = 8 \times 15$$

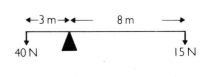

Figure 7

Changing the form of motion

Mechanisms are often used to change one kind of motion into another kind. Below are four methods of converting motion. You may find it helpful to try them out using modelling kits. Suitable kits include Fischertechnik UT1 and UT2, Meccano and the Lego technical set.

Rotary to linear, and linear to rotary

You often need to convert rotary motion to linear motion (*Figure 1*). For instance, you rotate a door handle to move the catch in a line. You rotate the knob on a radiator to move the valve in or out. You rotate the handle of a paper punch to push the punch down through the paper. You rotate the key on a G-cramp to open or close the cramp.

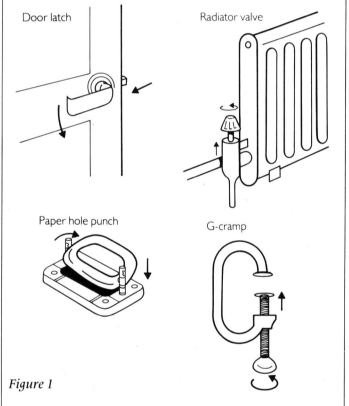

Door latch

Radiator valve

Paper hole punch

G-cramp

Figure 1

Some steep railways use a rack-and-pinion system (*Figure 2*). The **rack** has teeth, and lies along the railway track. The train has a **pinion**, or gear wheel. As the engine turns the pinion, the train is pulled along the track.

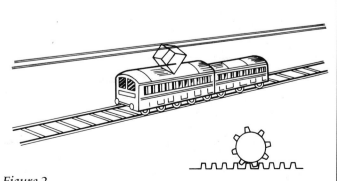

Figure 2

Another rotary to linear convertor is the cam and follower (*Figure 3*). The cam rotates. This makes the follower go up and then down. The follower falls because of its own weight or because there is pressure on it.

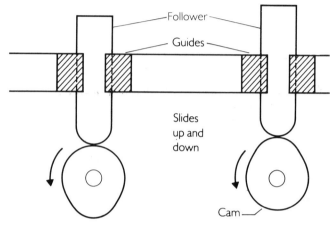

Follower

Guides

Slides up and down

Cam

Figure 3

Sometimes you want to convert linear motion to rotary motion. The most common example is the use of a piston, as in a car engine (*Figure 4*). The wheel which rotates pushes the ram between the guides. The length of movement of the ram is equal to twice the distance X shown in Figure 4.

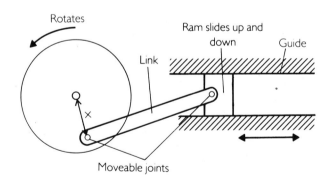

Rotates

Ram slides up and down

Guide

Link

X

Moveable joints

Figure 4

Reversing the direction

It is often necessary to convert clockwise motion to anticlockwise motion. This is easily done with two **gears**. As the input gear turns one way, the output gear turns the other (*Figure 5*).

It can also be done using two **pulleys** and a **drive belt**. The belt must be crossed between the pulleys, as in Figure 6.

Sometimes you don't want to reverse the motion, but need the gears. You can deal with this using another gear, called an **idler gear**. The idler gear is placed between the other two (*Figure 7*). The direction is now changed twice. If the input gear turns clockwise, the middle gear turns anticlockwise, and the output gear turns clockwise. A line of gears like this is called a **gear train**.

You can reverse linear motion too. The simplest way is to join two beams with a third. The third beam is pivoted at the middle – it is a lever. Look at Figure 8. If you pull the input beam, the output beam is pushed the other way.

Changing motion through 90°

Think about a hand drill, or a hand whisk. You turn the handle one way, and the drill bit or whisk turns at 90° to this. There are several ways of doing this.

You can use a flexible drive belt. This needs to be turned through 90° between one axle and the other (*Figure 9*). There is a danger that the belt will slip.

It is better to use gears. You can use two **bevel gears**, where the teeth are at 45° to the side of the gear (*Figure 10*). Or you can use a **worm gear**, which has a screw thread. This meshes with a **spur gear** on the other axle (*Figure 11*). The spur gear often has a large diameter.

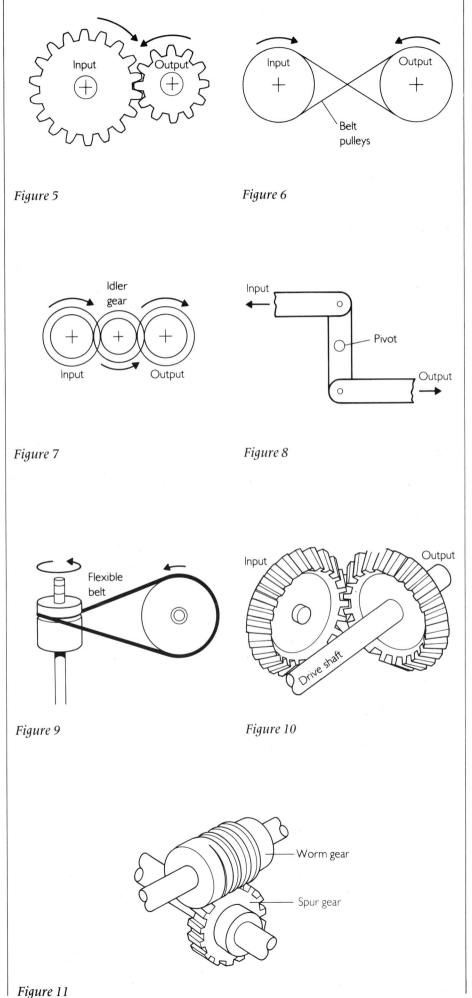

Figure 5

Figure 6

Figure 7

Figure 8

Figure 9

Figure 10

Figure 11

Changing the speed of motion

Many motors have only one speed. But other speeds are needed in machines that use the motors. So you need to be able to change speed. You can do this using pulleys or gears.

With pulleys, the speed is changed by using pulleys of different diameters (*Figure 1*). If a large pulley is connected by a belt to a small pulley, the small pulley turns faster. So if a large pulley drives a small one, there is an *increase* in speed. But if a small pulley drives a large one, there is a *decrease* in speed.

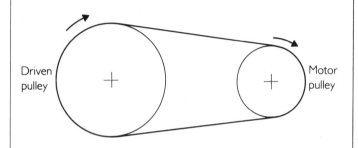

Figure 1

The pulley that drives the mechansism is the **motor pulley**. The pulley that is driven by the mechanism is the **driven pulley**. The change of speed depends on the diameters of these pulleys.

$$\frac{\text{Diameter of motor pulley}}{\text{Diameter of driven pulley}} = \frac{\text{speed of driven pulley}}{\text{speed of motor pulley}}$$

A motor pulley has a diameter of 25 mm. It rotates at 360 revolutions per minute (**rpm**). The driven pulley has a diameter of 45 mm. Then the *speed* of the driven pulley is found like this:

$$\text{Speed of driven pulley} =$$

$$\frac{25\,\text{mm}}{45\,\text{mm}} \times 360\,\text{rpm} = 200\,\text{rpm}$$

With gears, the speed is changed by using gears with different numbers of teeth (*Figure 2*). If a gear with a lot of teeth drives a gear with less teeth, there is an *increase* in speed. If a gear with a few teeth drives a gear with more teeth, there is a *decrease* in speed.

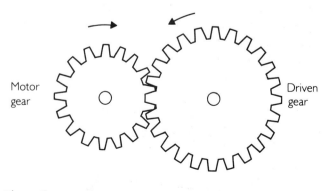

Figure 2

$$\frac{\text{Number of teeth on motor gear}}{\text{Number of teeth on driven gear}} =$$

$$\frac{\text{speed of driven gear}}{\text{speed of motor gear}}$$

A motor gear has 12 teeth. It rotates at 100 rpm. The driven gear has 24 teeth.

$$\text{Speed of driven gear} =$$

$$\frac{12\,\text{teeth}}{24\,\text{teeth}} \times 100\,\text{rpm} = 50\,\text{rpm}$$

The ratio of the driven gear speed to the motor gear speed is called the **gear ratio**.

$$\text{Gear ratio} = \frac{\text{number of teeth on driven gear}}{\text{number of teeth on motor gear}}$$

In the example above, the gear ratio is 24:12. This is the same as 2:1.

You often want to make a large change of speed. You may want to make the driven gear turn very much more quickly than the motor gear, or very much more slowly. You cannnot always do this with just one pair of gears. You may need to use several pairs of gears, one after the other (*Figure 3*). This is a gear train.

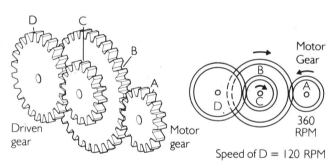

Figure 3

If two gears are on the same drive axle, they will turn at the same speed. They may be different sizes, but they turn at the same speed.

In Figure 3 there are four gears. The motor gear is *A*. This gear drives the gear *B*. *B* is on the same axle as *C*. When *B* turns, *C* turns as well. *C* turns at the same speed as *B*, because they are on the same axle. *C* drives the gear *D*. *D* is the final driven gear. Its speed is decided by the *two* gear ratios *A:B* and *C:D*.

Suppose *A* has 16 teeth, *B* has 32 teeth, *C* has 16 teeth and *D* has 24 teeth. The motor gear *A* turns at 360 rpm.

$$\text{The gear ratio} = \frac{A}{B} \times \frac{C}{D} = \frac{16}{32} \times \frac{16}{24} = \frac{1}{3}$$

The speed of the final driven gear *D* is one-third of the speed of the motor gear *A*. So the speed of *D* is $\frac{1}{3} \times 360$ rpm, which is 120 rpm.

Note that it is better to make a small gear drive a bigger gear than the other way round. The velocity ratio is better.

Modelling

It is often helpful to make a model of something you've designed. You can test the model and see whether it works as you expected. You may be able to improve your design before you make the real thing.

Commercial kits are very good for this. But they are not always adequate. Sometimes you want to make a model and the kit doesn't have the right pieces. So here are some ideas to help you make your models in other ways.

You can make a cranked shaft (*Figure 4*). This makes it easier to turn the axle. This is because the moment is greater (*page 61*). Because the handle is cranked, it is away from the centre of rotation. The bigger the diameter of the crank, the easier it is to turn.

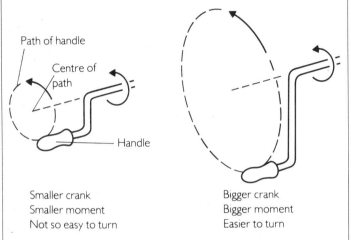

Smaller crank
Smaller moment
Not so easy to turn

Bigger crank
Bigger moment
Easier to turn

Figure 4

You can make small pulleys by sawing up pieces of dowel. To make larger pulleys you will need to cut discs of wood. The hole saw (*page 78*) will be helpful here.

You can turn the large wooden discs into cogs. Drill holes around the disc (*Figure 5*). The holes must be evenly spaced. Then cut out the waste wood, and round the corners. This is quite hard to do. You should not try to make cogs with more than 16 teeth in this way.

Mark the positions
of the holes

Cut out the
holes

Cut away the
waste

Round the corners

Figure 5

You can also make cogs by sticking pins or dowel pegs into the edge of a wooden disc (*Figure 6*).

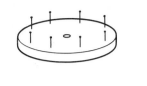
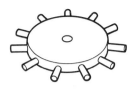

Figure 6

Simple metal gears can be made by attaching pieces of thin steel rod to a tin plate disc (*Figure 7*). You can attach them by soft soldering (*page 88*). These are effective in pairs, at 90° to each other. To use them the same way round, you need to bend the ends of the rods through 90°.

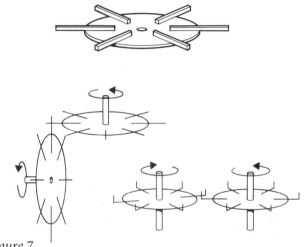

Figure 7

You can make cogs by gluing strips of wood to the edge of wooden discs (*Figure 8*). Or you can saw slots in the edge of the disc, and push in thin pieces of plywood.

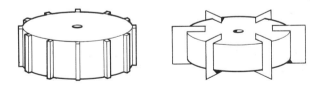

Figure 8

You could use these cogs with a rack. To make the rack, glue strips of wood to a long piece of wood (*Figure 9*). The rack will work better if you round the corners slightly.

These are just a few ideas. You will probably have ideas of your own.

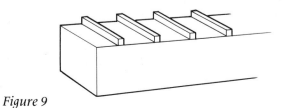

Figure 9

Kinds of energy

Energy is vital to us, and always will be. A lot of our energy comes from natural resources – coal, oil and gas. These are running out. But we still use them to provide about 90% of the energy for heating, lighting, transport and power in factories. We must be careful not to waste energy.

But these are not the only sources of energy. All energy on Earth comes originally from the sun. A lot is used by growing plants. Some of the plants are eaten by animals, including humans. Other plants decay, and eventually form coal or oil.

There is energy in **light**. You feel warm when the sun is shining. There is energy in running **water**. Rivers and streams can be made to turn water mills, and to operate hydro-electric power stations. There is energy in **wind**. Windmills used to be common, but there are only a few still working now.

Energy from the sun is 'trapped' by plants which are then eaten by animals. **Animals** can be used to do work. Fuels like wood, coal, oil and gas all come from **plants**. Their energy is released by burning them. At first people used **fire** just to provide heat and light. But they gradually learnt to control fire. Now we can use energy from burning to make machines work. One of the best examples is the steam boiler. Coal is burnt, and the energy released heats water. The water turns into steam, and the steam builds up pressure. This force can be used to move things. For example, the steam can be used to move a train. Or it can be used to generate **electricity**. Then the electricity can be used.

Energy cannot be created. Nor can it be destroyed. But it can change its form. There are lots of examples of energy changing form. We have just seen that heat can make steam, and steam can make electricity. Electricity can make light, as in an ordinary light bulb. Light can be used to heat water, as is done in some solar panels.

Each time energy changes form, some of it is lost. No method of energy conversion is 100% efficient. For example, when water energy turns a water wheel, some of the energy is lost by friction as the wheel turns. When gas is burnt on a gas cooker to provide heat, some of the energy is lost as light. If you keep converting the form, you lose more and more of the energy. It is best to do the conversion in one step if possible.

People are now looking for new sources of energy. One of the best known new sources is **nuclear** energy. Here the energy is released by combining or splitting atoms. Another source is **solar** energy. This is energy from the sun that is trapped directly in solar cells.

Forms of energy

To make a good working article, you will certainly need a lot of human energy! You may also use **mechanical energy** or **electrical energy**.

Mechanical energy

There are two types of mechanical energy. They are often used together.

An object can have energy because of its position. This is called **potential energy**. The energy is stored in the object until the object is released. For example, a compressed spring has potential energy (*Figure 1*).

Compressed   Released

Figure 1

When it is released, it expands. A stretched elastic band has potential energy (*Figure 2*). When it is released, it contracts. A lift at the tenth floor of a building has potential energy. When it is released, it drops.

Released

Stretched

Figure 2

An object can also have energy because of its movement. This is called **kinetic energy**. You need energy to stop something that is moving. For example, you need brakes to stop a moving bicycle (*Figure 3*) and you need force to return a tennis ball over the net.

Bike going down hill

Figure 3

Potential energy can be turned into kinetic energy. A stretched catapult has potential energy. When it is released, the pebble gains kinetic energy (*Figure 4*).

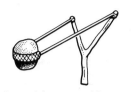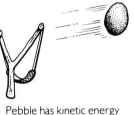

Catapult has potential energy   Pebble has kinetic energy

Figure 4

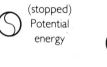

Kinetic energy (rising)   (stopped) Potential energy   Kinetic energy (falling)

Figure 5

Also, kinetic energy can be turned into potential energy. If you throw a ball in the air, it has kinetic energy while it is moving. It loses this kinetic energy as it rises, and it stops. The kinetic energy has turned into potential energy, because the ball is now higher than it was. It then falls back, and the potential energy becomes kinetic energy again (*Figure 5*).

Electrical energy

The only natural form of electricial energy is lightning. This cannot be trapped and used. Most electrical energy is made from other natural sources, such as those described on the opposite page.

Electrical energy can be stored in **batteries**. There are *dry* batteries, which are used in torches and radios. And there are *wet* batteries, which are used in car engines. Both sorts of battery use chemical energy to create electricity. Chemical energy is a kind of potential energy. Batteries are often used to drive motors, which then have kinetic energy (*Figure 6*).

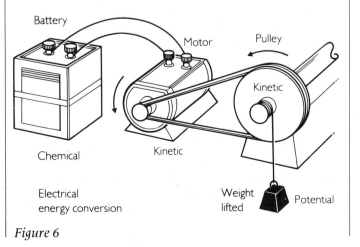

Battery

Motor

Pulley

Kinetic

Chemical

Kinetic

Electrical energy conversion

Weight lifted

Potential

Figure 6

Using energy

You often need to store energy and release it later in a controlled way. A simple exercise is to make a cotton reel climb a slope. You can do this with a rubber band, a match stick and a piece of dowel (*Figure 1*). The rubber band is twisted, which gives it stored potential energy. It is released under control of the piece of dowel. The potential energy is converted to kinetic energy.

Here are two projects. You may be able to apply the same principles in other projects. The projects here may give you ideas of your own.

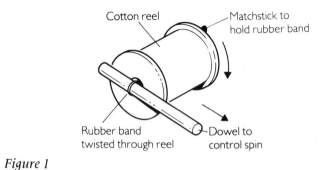

Figure 1

Application 1   To project a small ball

Here are just six ways of projecting a ball. Perhaps you will think of others.

1

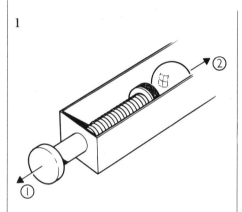

The handle is pulled, as shown by the arrow. This compresses the spring. When the handle is released, the ball is projected.

2

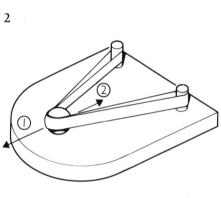

The elastic is stretched. This puts it in tension. When it is released, it contracts and projects the ball.

3

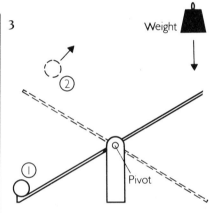

The weight is dropped. It rotates the seesaw on the pivot. The other end of the seesaw projects the ball.

4

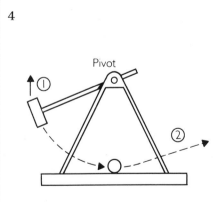

The pendulum is raised. When it is released, it falls and strikes the ball. This projects the ball.

5

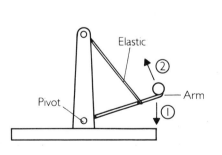

The arm is pulled back and down. This stretches the elastic. When the arm is released, the elastic contracts. The arm rises and projects the ball.

6

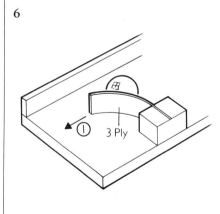

The strip is made of flexible plastic. It is pulled back, which puts it under tension. When it is released, it straightens and projects the ball.

Using energy

Application 2 To move a vehicle along a flat surface

These are just five ways of moving a model vehicle. There are many other ways of doing the same thing.

1

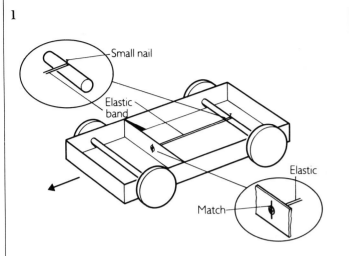

A rubber band is attached to the frame and to the back axle. The back axle is fixed to the wheels. The wheels are turned to wind the rubber band round the axle. When they are released, the vehicle moves forward quickly.

2

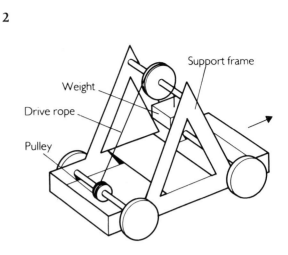

A drive rope is attached to the back axle. The rope is wound around the axle. The other end passes over a pulley on a frame. The end is attached to a weight above the vehicle. As the weight falls, it pulls the rope. This turns the axle, and the vehicle moves forward.

3

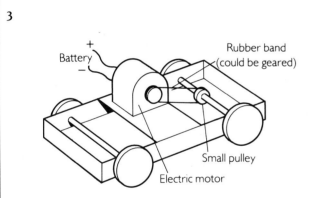

A small electric motor is mounted on the frame. It is driven by a battery in the vehicle. The motor is connected to the back axle by a drive belt (a rubber band) or gears. As the motor turns, the vehicle moves forward slowly.

4

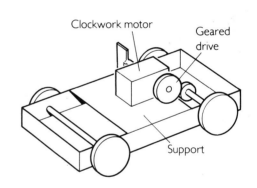

A small clockwork motor is mounted on the frame. It is connected to the back axle by gears. The motor is wound up. When it is released, the vehicle moves forward.

5

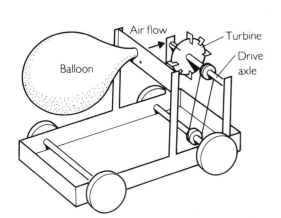

The vehicle has two upright frames. One frame holds an axle connected to the back axle by means of a drive belt (a rubber band). On the axle is a disc with paddles (a **turbine**). On the other frame is an inflated balloon. The balloon is held in a slot. As the balloon deflates, the air from it turns the turbine. This turns the axle, and this turns the wheel axle. The vehicle moves forward.

Note the combined use of structures, mechanisms and energy in these projects.

Choice of material

Whatever you design, it will eventually be made in some **material**. There are lots of materials that are available in nature. These are *natural* materials. There are also materials created by people. These are *synthetic* materials. Some materials are natural, but are *altered* to be more useful.

Natural materials include clay, wood and metal. Synthetic materials include plastic, glass and concrete. Altered natural materials include leather (made from the skins of animals), fabrics (made by twisting and weaving plant fibres) and paper (made by drying sheets of plant fibres).

You may need to use different materials for different articles. As a designer, you must decide which material to use. You might want to use several materials in the same article. To decide this, ask yourself questions about the material you need. Here are some examples.

* *Should it be hard or soft?*
* *Should it be heavy or light?*
* *Should it be rigid or flexible?*
* *Will it be in blocks or sheets?*
* *Does the colour matter?*
* *Does it have to conduct electricity?*

Now you know what sort of material you need. Here are four more key questions.

* *Will the chosen material do what you want?*
* *Is your chosen material available?*
* *Can you afford the chosen material?*
* *Do you know how to work with the chosen material?*

Technical vocabulary

Here are some words used to describe materials. You may find them helpful.

* *A material that resists being pulled apart has* **tensile strength**.
* *A material that resists being crushed has* **compressive strength**.
* *A material that resists cuts and scratches is* **hard**.
* *A material that resists breaking is* **tough**.
* *A material that breaks easily is* **brittle**.
* *A material that bends easily is* **pliable**.
* *A material that can be worked into shape is* **malleable**.
* *A material that can be eaten away (perhaps by rust) is* **corrodible**.
* *A material that transfers heat has* **heat conductivity**.
* *A material that transfers electricity has* **electrical conductivity**.

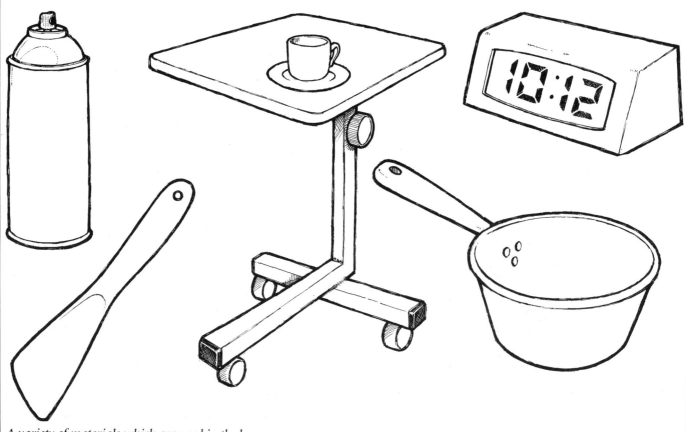

A variety of materials which are used in the home

Metals

Metals are found naturally in the earth. But they are usually mixed or combined with something else. A metal in the earth is part of an **ore**. The ore is dug out of the earth. Then the metal is extracted from the ore.

Metals are sometimes used in a pure form. But they may be mixed with something else to change their properties for example malleability. Steel is a mixture of iron and carbon. Brass is a mixture of copper and zinc. Soft solder is a mixture of tin and lead. Mixtures of metals are called **alloys**.

The two metals most used in industry are steel and aluminium. Steel is extracted from iron ore (*Figure 1*). Aluminium is extracted from a natural ore called bauxite (*Figure 2*).

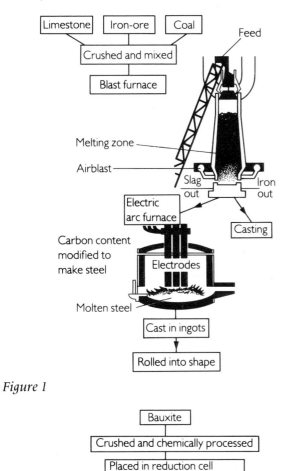

Figure 1

Figure 2

Properties and identification

There are two families of metals. **Ferrous** metals contain iron and **non-ferrous** metals contain no iron. There are many different useful metals. Here are some notes about the most commonly used metals.

Steel is a mixture of iron and carbon, with small amounts of other substances. The properties of steel depend on the ratio of the things in it.

Mild steel has 0.3% carbon. It is grey in colour, cheap, and commonly used. It corrodes easily. Mild steel is used for nuts, bolts and car bodies. It is good for project work.

Cast iron has 3% carbon. It is dark grey in colour. It is more expensive and less often used than mild steel. It is hard, brittle and heavy. Cast iron is used for pans, vices and engine blocks. It is unsuitable for project work.

Stainless steel has 1% carbon. It also has 18% chromium and 8% nickel. It is silver in colour, and shines. It is expensive. It is hard, and difficult to work. It does not stain or corrode. Stainless steel is used for sinks, kitchen utensils and pipes. It is unsuitable for most project work.

Tin plate is made by coating mild steel with tin. Mild steel corrodes easily. But coating protects it from corrosion. Tin plate is strong, and can be bent to shape. But it can easily be scratched. When scratched, the mild steel underneath begins to corrode. Tin plate is silver in colour and shiny. It is cheap. Tin plate is used to make tin cans. Useful for project work.

Aluminium is light, soft and malleable. It is light grey in colour. Sheets of aluminium may be shiny. Aluminium resists corrosion, and conducts heat and electricity. It is fairly cheap. It cannot be soldered. Aluminium is used to make window frames, kitchen pans, foil and aircraft. It is good for project work.

Copper is tough and malleable. It is reddish brown in colour, and shines when polished. It resists corrosion, and conducts heat and electricity well. It is expensive. Copper is used for electrical cables, radiators and water pipes. It is good for small projects.

Brass is an alloy of copper and zinc. These can be mixed in different proportions to make different kinds of brass. Brass is hard but easy to work. It is yellow in colour and shines when polished. It resists corrosion. It is expensive. Brass is used for plaques, ornaments and water taps. It is good for small projects.

Plastics

Plastics are fairly new materials. They have been developed during the last forty years or so. They were originally made from natural substances, such as animals, insects and plants. Today most plastics are made from crude oil. Some coal and gas are also used.

Plastics can now be created with almost any desired properties. They are made by a complex process of refining and combining. Most plastics are made by joining together long carbon-based molecules. These long strings are called **chains** or **polymers**.

When made, plastics can be processed in different ways.

Extrusion   Plastic is forced through a shaped nozzle. Extrusion is used for guttering and cable.

Blow moulding   Plastic is blown against the sides of a mould. Blow moulding is used for bottles.

Injection moulding   Plastic is injected into a mould. Injection moulding is used for kitchen bowls.

Calendering   Plastic is rolled into very thin sheets. Calendering is used for film and bags.

Vacuum forming   Plastic is sucked into moulds. Vacuum forming is used for baths and cartons.

Rotational forming   Plastic is rotated while it is being shaped. Rotational forming is used for footballs.

Compression moulding   Plastic is compressed into moulds. Compression moulding is used for handles and knobs.

Thermoplastics

Thermoplastics are one kind of plastic. They can be softened by heating, and hardened by cooling. This heating and cooling can be repeated, so thermoplastics are not used for articles that need to withstand heat in use. Thermoplastics cut cleanly, scratch easily and become soft at low temperatures.

There are different sorts of thermoplastic.

Polyethylene, or **polythene** may have a high or low density. High-density polyethylene is stiff and strong. It is used for bleach bottles and milk crates. Low-density polyethylene is tough and flexible. It is used for plastic bags and washing-up liquid bottles. Both sorts of polyethylene resist chemical corrosion. Both sorts can be dyed various colours.

Polyvinylchloride, or **PVC** may be rigid or flexible. Rigid PVC is stiff, hard and light. It is a good electrical insulator. It is used for pipes, guttering and shoes. Flexible PVC is softer. It is used for coating paper and cloth. Both sorts of PVC are available in various colours.

Polystyrene   is stiff and hard. It is used for disposable food containers. Expanded polystyrene is white and very light. It is a good heat insulator. It is used for insulating tiles and packaging.

Polymethylmethacrylate, or **acrylic**   is stiff and hard. It is rather like glass, but does not shatter. It is used for illuminated signs and for baths. It is available in various colours.

Thermosets

Thermosets are a different kind of plastic. They can be moulded initially by heat, but then set. They cannot be reformed. Thermosets are used for articles that must withstand heat. Thermosets will slip when cut, stay hard and only blister when heated.

There are different sorts of thermoset.

Polyester resin   is hard and brittle. It may be strengthened by laminating it with fibres (glass reinforced fibre – GRP). It is used for boat hulls and garden furniture.

Phenol formaldehyde   is dark, hard and brittle. It is a good heat insulator. It is used for saucepan handles and cheap electrical fittings.

Urea formaldehyde   is hard and brittle. It is a good heat insulator. It is light in colour, usually white. It is used for cheap white electrical fittings and waterproof wood glues.

Melamine formaldehyde   is strong and hard. It is a good heat insulator. It resists staining. It is more expensive than the other sorts of formaldehyde. It is used for decorating laminates, plastic tableware, resin paints and expensive electrical fittings. It is available in various colours.

Wood

Growing trees need several things. They need water and mineral salts. These are absorbed through the roots. They need carbon dioxide. This is absorbed through the leaves. They need sunlight. The energy in the sunlight converts the carbon dioxide, water and minerals into other chemicals that the trees need.

Look at Figure 1. It shows a section through a tree **trunk**. You can see the various parts of the tree. On the outside is the **bark**. Beneath the bark is the new, living wood – the **sapwood**. In the middle of the trunk is the old, dead wood – the **heartwood**. A new ring of wood grows just below the bark each year. In the section, you can see **annual rings**. Water and minerals are carried through the trunk in **medullary rays**. These are rather like the arteries in animals.

Trees are cut down, or **felled**, when required. They are transported to the saw mill, often by river. The trunks are sawn into **planks**. Planks are dried out, or **seasoned**. This is done in a kiln or in the open air.

The wood from broadleaved trees, such as oak, beech and ash, is **hardwood**. The wood from conifers, such as pine and cedar, is **softwood** (*Figure 2*). Wood may be used in its natural form, when it is usually called **timber**. Or it may be processed to make other materials.

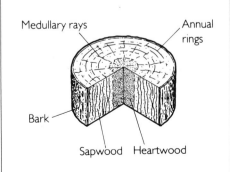

Figure 1

Natural wood

Softwood

Redwood is strong and the grain is straight. It is honey-coloured or reddish brown. It is cheap and readily available. Redwood is used for general construction work.

Red cedar is light and the grain is straight. It is easy to work. It is reddish brown. Red cedar is more expensive than redwood, and not as strong. It is readily available. It is used for windows, doors and panels.

Hardwood

African mahoganies are hard and strong. There are different mahoganies, including **utile** and **sapele**. They are reddish brown or pinkish. Mahoganies are cheap and readily available. They are easy to work, and produce a good finish. They are used for furniture.

Beech is very hard and strong. It is heavy and difficult to work. It is pinkish brown with flecks in it. Beech is fairly cheap and readily available. It is used for kitchen furniture and kitchen tools.

Teak is hard, strong and durable. It is not easy to work. It is golden brown. Teak is expensive. It is used in high-class indoor and outdoor furniture.

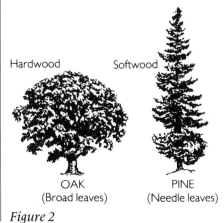

Figure 2

Processed wood

Veneers are thin sheets cut from logs (*Figure 3*). Veneers of expensive wood are used to cover cheaper, less attractive wood.

Rotary cut (cheap form)   Slice cutting (expensive)

Figure 3

Plywood is made by gluing together cheap veneers. Three sheets of veneer form **three-ply** (*Figure 4*). It can be made in various thicknesses. It is heavy, strong and expensive. Plywood is used in construction work.

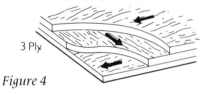

3 Ply

Figure 4

Blockboard is made by gluing together strips of softwood. These are covered with veneer (*Figure 5*). Blockboard is strong and durable, but rather expensive. It is used for modern furniture and shelves.

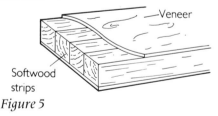

Veneer

Softwood strips

Figure 5

Chipboard is made by gluing and compressing particles of wood. It is often covered with veneer. Chipboard is rather brittle, difficult to join, but cheap. It is used for cheap furniture.

Hardboard is made by pulping and compressing waste wood. One surface is textured, the other is smooth. It is made in thin sheets, and is cheap. Hardboard is used to cover hidden parts of cheap furniture.

Safety

When you have designed an article and chosen the material, you can start to make it. You will use various tools. Some are electrically operated, some are hand operated. You need different tools for different materials. Each material has its own characteristics, and must be worked in the correct way.

Tools – hand tools and machine tools – can be dangerous. But you will be quite safe if you learn to use them properly. If you work carefully, you will protect yourself, your friends and the equipment you use. Here are some basic rules of **safety**.

* ★ *Always wear protective clothing.*
* ★ *Do not allow clothing (such as sleeves or ties), long hair or jewellery to hang loosely. These things can easily get trapped in a machine.*
* ★ *Wear strong shoes while working, in case you drop something hot or heavy on your foot.*
* ★ *Never rush about the workshop. Always concentrate on what you are doing. Accidents may be caused by people running or pushing. Accidents may happen while you are carrying tools or materials. Be especially careful with hot materials.*
* ★ *If you are using a cutting tool, make sure that it is really sharp and correctly set. Ask for help if you are not sure. Keep your hands away from the cutting edge. It usually helps if you cramp the material to the bench.*
* ★ *When using a machine, always protect your eyes by wearing a visor or goggles. Check that the guards on the machine are in position. Never touch parts of the machine that are moving.*
* ★ *Be very careful if you use acid. Protect your eyes.*
* ★ *If you have an accident, tell your teacher immediately.*
* ★ *If you find a tool or machine that is broken or faulty, tell your teacher immediately.*

Remember, if in doubt ask your teacher.

Protective clothing

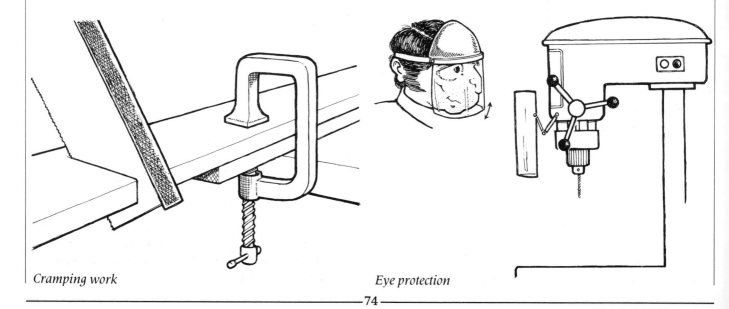

Cramping work

Eye protection

Marking out

Before you can make something, you need to select your material. With the material in front of you, you can start to mark the design on it. This process is called **marking out**.

It is important to mark out carefully. There are two reasons. First, careful marking out will save you time and disappointment. It is better to get it right first time than to have to start again. Second, careful marking out will save you material. All materials cost money. So you must use them economically. For example, suppose you are going to cut a circle from a big rectangular piece of wood. You should mark the circle in the corner of the rectangle, not in the middle. If you cut the circle from the middle, you will waste a lot of wood.

You need to think about the material you are using. For example, wood has a grain running in one direction. You must mark out your design so that the grain will run correctly across the finished article (*Figure 1*).

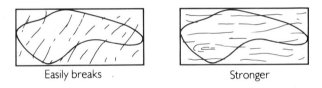

| Easily breaks | Stronger |

Figure 1

The marks you make must be clear. With steel, coat the metal with marking blue and scratch the design using a **scriber**. With aluminium and copper, draw the design with a scriber or a **pencil**. With tin plate, use a pencil only – the scriber would cut the protective tin layer. With plastics, draw with a **spirit felt pen**: leave protective paper on if possible. With wood, draw with a pencil or special tool.

Marking out using a template

It is difficult to draw an irregular shape accurately. Draw it first on paper. Then cut out the shape. You now have a paper **template**. You can attach this to the material with weak **glue** or double-sided **sticky tape**. Then you can cut round the template to create your shape. If you want several pieces the same shape, it may be better to make a wooden or plastic template to draw round.

Starting to mark out

A lot of designs are drawn on materials by measuring the distance from a straight edge. So before you start drawing the design, mark a straight line on the material. Then cut this to make a straight edge.

With wood, you also need to mark the **face side** and the **face edge** (*Figure 2*).

Figure 2

Marking at 90° to a straight edge

You need a tool called a **try square** or **engineers' square**. One part of this is flat, and lies along the surface of the material. The other part is thicker, and lies along the edge of the material. Place the square firmly against the edge of the material, and mark a line along the straight edge of the square (*Figure 3*).

You can mark the line using a pencil or scriber. When working with wood, it is helpful to mark with a knife which cuts across the fibres in the wood. This helps to make a clean cut later.

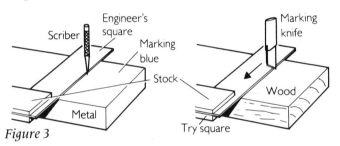

Figure 3

Marking parallel to a straight edge

You need a **marking gauge** or **odd-leg calipers**. Keep the stepped point of the calipers and the stock of the gauge against the edge of the material (*Figure 4*).

This is difficult to do. Practise drawing parallel lines on an unwanted bit of material.

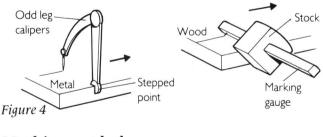

Figure 4

Marking out holes

Figure 5

Mark the centre of the hole. Make a small indentation at this centre. With wood, use a **bradawl**. With metal, use a **centre punch**. With plastics, use a scriber. Now use dividers to mark the hole (*Figure 5*).

Sawing

Sawing is a relatively quick method of removing material. There are many different types of saw. All saws have teeth that tear away the material being sawn. The teeth are set so that the saw will not get stuck (*Figure 1*). The shape and size of the teeth are chosen to suit the material. Teeth usually point away

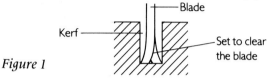

Figure 1

from the handle. They cut the material on the push stroke. One exception is the coping saw, described below.

Sawing technique

Here are some general notes about sawing.

★ *Always support the work in a vice or cramp. Hold thin pieces of material close to the point of cutting. In some cases extra support with waste material will be necessary. For wood, you may find a* **bench hook** *useful (Figure 2).*

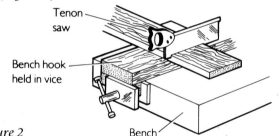

Figure 2

★ *Always try to make straight cuts vertically.*
★ *Stand with your hand and arm in line with the saw cut.*
★ *Make sure that at least three teeth are in contact with the material all the time. If less teeth are in contact, they may break. It is best to use small teeth for hard materials, and large teeth for soft materials.*
★ *Use your thumb at the side of the blade as a guide when you start the cut.*
★ *Always use the full length of the blade.*
★ *When you are sawing along a line, saw slightly on the waste side of the line (Figure 3).*

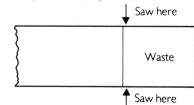

Figure 3

★ *When coming to the end of the cut, support the work underneath. If you do not, the material may crack and splinter.*

Kinds of saw

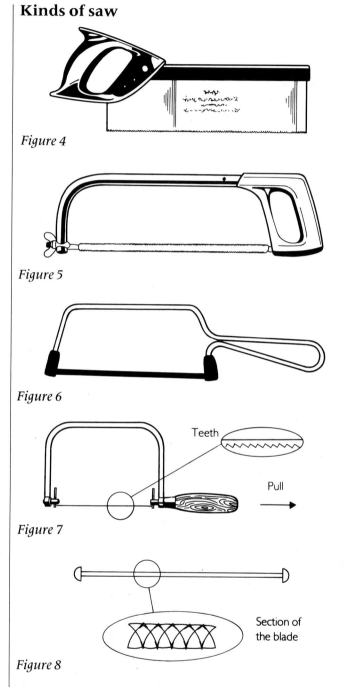

Figure 4

Figure 5

Figure 6

Figure 7

Figure 8

Tenon saws are used to make straight cuts through wood and plastic (*Figure 4*).

Hacksaws are used to make straight cuts through metal and plastic (*Figure 5*). There are small hacksaws called **junior hacksaws** (*Figure 6*).

Coping saws are used to make curved cuts through wood and plastic (*Figure 7*). Coping saws cut on the pull stroke – this keeps the frame in tension.

Abrafiles are used to make curved cuts through metal and plastic. The blade is rather like a file, and is held in a hacksaw frame (*Figure 8*).

Filing and planing

Small amounts of unwanted material can be removed in several ways, depending on the material.

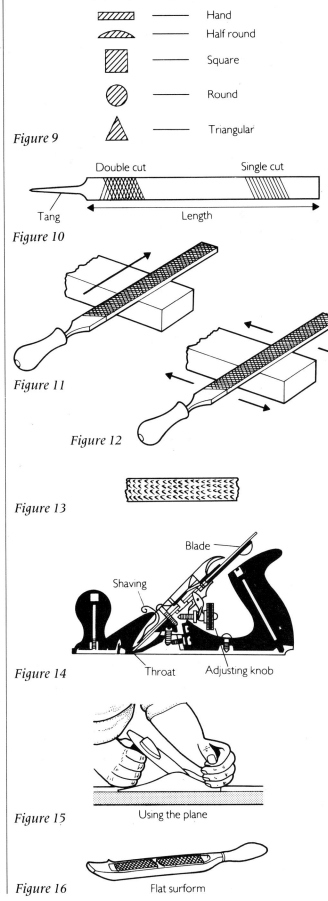

⬛	———	Hand
⬗	———	Half round
◩	———	Square
◎	———	Round
◭	———	Triangular

Figure 9

Figure 10

Double cut   Single cut

Tang   Length

Figure 11

Figure 12

Figure 13

Blade

Shaving

Throat   Adjusting knob

Figure 14

Using the plane

Figure 15

Figure 16   Flat surform

Files

These are commonly used on metal and plastic. (They can also be used for wood.)

Files remove small particles of material. There is a range of shapes (*Figure 9*). Other parts of the file vary too (*Figure 10*). Files vary in coarseness: **bastard files** are the coarsest, next **second-cut files**, then **smooth files**. You must always use a file with a handle on when filing.

For normal filing, hold the file at each end. Push the file across the material. It only cuts on the forward stroke (*Figure 11*). This is called **crossfiling**.

To give a smooth finish, push the file sideways up and down the material (*Figure 12*). This is called **drawfiling**.

Sometimes small pieces of material stick in the file. This is known as **pinning**. Use a **file card** to clean the file. You may need to put some chalk on the file to stop it pinning. Be especially careful to avoid pinning when you are filing plastic.

Rasps

These may be used on wood.

Rasps are similar to coarse files. They have individual teeth (*Figure 13*). They are used for rough shaping, especially for sculpture.

Planes

These may be used on wood.

Planes have sharp blades that cut a thin layer of wood from the work. There are many types of plane which use different holding methods. The most common is the **smoothing plane** (*Figure 14*).

Make sure that the wood is firmly held while you plane it. Place the plane on the wood, and push it in the direction of the grain (*Figure 15*). If the first cut is rough, try the other direction – you may be planing against the grain. The plane should leave a flat surface. If in doubt, ask your teacher. The plane is difficult to use and needs to be set carefully.

Surforms

These may be used on wood.

Surforms are held like files and rasps, but they cut like planes (*Figure 16*). The shavings pass through the blade, so the surform does not clog. Surforms remove wood quickly, but leave a rough surface. Be careful not to tear the edge of the wood.

Drilling

There are many types of **drill**. They all work by rotating a cutting edge which chisels into the material making a cylindrical hole. The most common sort of drill is the **twist drill**. The twist drill has a **cutting edge**, a spiral groove (the **flute**) to release the chips and a **straight shank** to hold the drill. Drills may be electrically-driven or hand-driven.

Figure 1

Drilling technique

Here are some general points about drilling.

★ *Mark clearly the point where you wish to drill. On steel, use a centre punch.*
★ *Make sure that the work is held firmly.*
★ *Make sure that the drill will not damage the bench or vice when it has gone through the work.*
★ *Plastics and man-made boards may crack or tear, especially underneath. Cramp some waste material beneath the work to prevent this (Figure 2).*

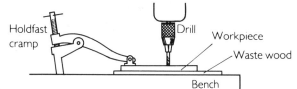

Figure 2

★ *When drilling deep holes, remove the drill from time to time. Clear the flute of waste material, to prevent clogging and overheating.*

Hand drilling

You need to concentrate while drilling by hand. Try to keep the drill vertical. Make sure that the hand drill is always supported when the drill is in the hole – otherwise the drill bit may bend or break (*Figure 3*).

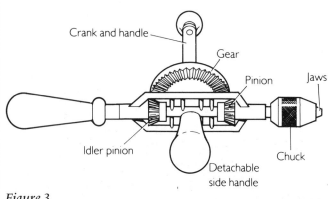

Figure 3

Machine drilling

With an electric drilling machine, you can adjust the speed of drilling. The larger the drill bit, the slower it must turn. When drilling mild steel you should use **cutting fluid** to keep the drill bit cool. When drilling plastic be especially careful not to let the bit overheat, or the plastic may melt.

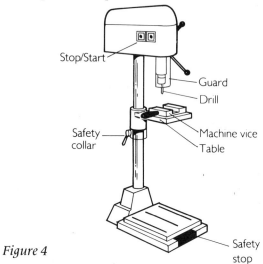

Figure 4

The drilling machine is one of the first machines you will use in the school workshop (*Figure 4*). Don't use it without permission from your teacher. It is quite safe provided that you observe the safety precautions: keep the work held firmly, use the drilling machine guard and use eye protection.

Countersink drilling

Some screws have bevelled heads, so that they can sit level with the surface of the material they hold. After drilling the cylindrical hole for the screw, you need to open out the end of the hole to a V-section. You can do this with a **countersink drill** (*Figure 5*).

Hole or disc drilling

You can use a special kind of drill to make larger holes. This drill is called a **hole saw** (*Figure 6*). This drill is also very useful for making discs or wheels.

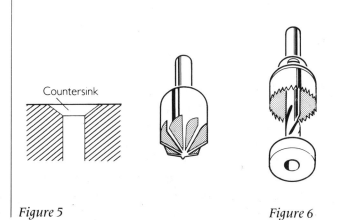

Figure 5   *Figure 6*

Shearing and chiselling

Shears and chisels are two more tools that may be used to shape material. A pair of **shears** consist of two blades. These are brought together to slice through the material (*Figure 7*). Ordinary scissors work in this way. A **chisel** has only one blade which shears through material.

Shearing technique

The shears you will use are called **tinsnips** (*Figure 8*). As their name suggests, they are used to cut tin plate. They can also cut aluminium sheet and copper sheet.

To operate tinsnips, you need to press on both arms of the tool at the same time. It helps if you put one arm of the snips in a vice and press on the other arm (*Figure 9*). Do not put the sheet too far into the shears. If you do, you will find it difficult to cut the sheet. Do not close the shears completely when cutting, as this may make a small mark on the work.

Be very careful not to trap your fingers! A bench shearing machine requires even more care. You should not use one without permission from your teacher.

Chiselling technique

Chisels can be used on wood or metal, but here we shall look at chisels for cutting wood only.

Figure 10 shows a bevel-edged chisel. The blade is made of hardened steel. The handle is made of boxwood, ash or shatterproof plastic. The blade must have a straight, sharp cutting edge.

Chisels are usually hand-held. Chiselling by hand is also called **paring**. Timber can be pared *along* the grain or *across* the grain. If you pare *along* the grain, you have little control. The timber is likely to split and tear (*Figure 11*). It is better to use a plane where possible. If you pare *across* the grain, it is easier to control the chisel. Instead of making splinters, you make neat pieces of fibre that curl away from the wood (*Figure 12*).

Here are some general points about chiselling.

* *Always make sure that the work is firmly cramped.*
* *Keep both hands behind the cutting edge.*
* *Never cut towards your body.*
* *Cut across the grain whenever possible.*
* *When cutting a groove, use the correct width of chisel. First cut the limits of your chiselling with a saw. Then pare from both sides of the groove. This will leave clean edges (Figure 13).*

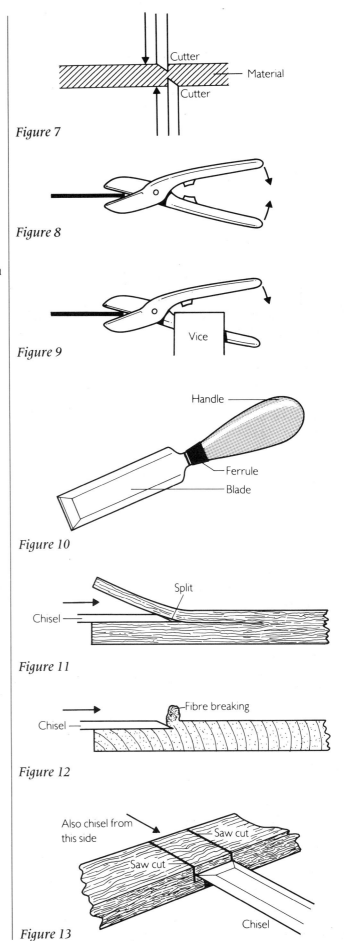

Figure 7

Figure 8

Figure 9

Figure 10

Figure 11

Figure 12

Figure 13

Finishing

When you have made your project you should use a suitable finish. This will protect it and make it last longer, and it will improve the appearance.

Before applying extra materials to the surface of an article, make sure that it has been cleaned and finished.

Abrasives

Articles can be made absolutely smooth using **abrasive cloths** and **papers**. These are finer than files and surforms, so they make the surface smoother. Each abrasive comes in various **grades** of coarseness. Here are some general points to remember.

★ *Clean all inner surfaces as you assemble the article.*
★ *Start with a coarse abrasive and work through the grades to finish with a fine abrasive.*
★ *Whenever possible, support the abrasive material on a wooden block with slightly rounded corners (Figure 1). This helps to maintain the shape of the article.*

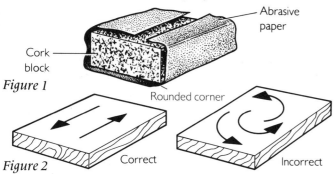

Cork block
Abrasive paper
Rounded corner

Figure 1

Correct
Incorrect

Figure 2

★ *Always use the abrasive in the same direction (Figure 2). When smoothing wood, work along the grain.*

Choose the abrasive to suit the material.

Steel   Use **emery cloth**. There are three common grades – coarse (1½), medium (F) and smooth (O). Add a little oil to the fine grade to give a mirror finish.

Copper   Clean in a **pickling bath** of sulphuric acid (1 part) and water (12 parts). (Wear eye protection when working with acid!) Then remove the copper article and wash it in water. Next clean it with

pumice powder and a **water of Ayr stone**. Finally polish the article on a polishing machine or by hand, using metal polish.

Plastic   Use **silicone carbide paper**, also known as **wet-and-dry paper**. There are three common grades – fine (100), medium (200) and smooth (400). This paper is best used wet. It creates a smooth, matt finish. You can polish the article with a **fine chrome cleaning paste**.

Wood   Use glass paper. The three common grades here are coarse (S2), medium (F2) and smooth (O). If you coat the wood with a **sealer**, you can also use **steel wool** to give a smooth surface.

Finishes

Steel   This is difficult to finish neatly. You can smear oil on it. You can heat the steel, dip it in old oil to give a black finish, and then polish it with black shoe polish. Or you can **paint** it, provided it is completely free of oil and grease. To paint steel, apply a priming coat first. Then apply an undercoat, and finally a topcoat. Don't forget to clean the brushes!

Tinplate   If you want a surface finish, it is best to paint tinplate. Use three coats, as for steel.

Copper   This is often simply polished. You may apply a clear **lacquer**.

Aluminium   This is usually simply polished.

Plastic   This too is just polished.

Wood   You can paint timber, using three coats as for steel. If the wood is for use outdoors, you may preserve it with creosote. If the wood is attractive with an interesting grain, you may apply a clear **varnish**. This may be lacquer or polyurethane. Or you could **stain** the wood, to darken it or bring out the features. Some woods, especially teak, are best finished with oil.

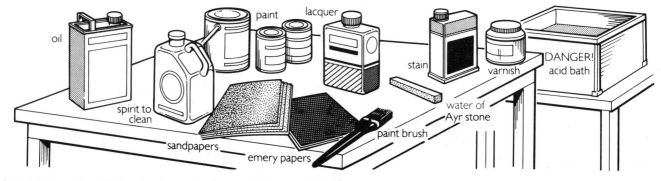

oil
paint
lacquer
spirit to clean
sandpapers
emery papers
paint brush
water of Ayr stone
stain
varnish
DANGER! acid bath

Deforming metals

Articles can be shaped by cutting them out of larger blocks – this is what has been described in the last few pages. But articles can also be made by changing the shape of a piece of material. This process is called **deformation.**

Metals can be deformed after heating. This is called **forging.** They can also be deformed when cold, by levering, hammering or pressing. In this book we look only at cold deformation.

Deforming techniques

Bending strips
You can bend lengths of cold mild steel fairly easily, provided they are not more than 6 mm thick. Hold them in a vice while bending them. You may need to use a mallet. You cannot easily straighten a strip that has been bent in the wrong place, so you must bend it accurately first time. It is a good idea to produce a full-size drawing of the final shape. Then you can measure the metal as you work. There are two special tools to help with bending – the **peg jig** and the **lever jig** (*Figure 3*).

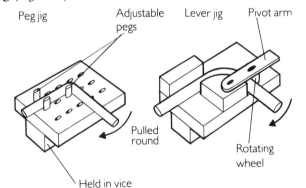

Figure 3

Bending sheets along lines
Line bending is used for bends along straight lines. Hold the metal sheet in a folding bar, and grip the bar in a vice (*Figure 4*). Now hammer the metal to bend it over the bar. Use a mallet with a raw-hide or nylon head. For some work, you may find a block of wood more useful than a folding bar.

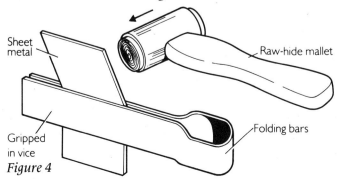

Figure 4

Bending sheets into complex shapes
Three-dimensional forming, or **beaten metalwork**, is used for sheets of copper and aluminium. First soften the sheet by annealing it (see below). Then mark out the design with a pencil. Hold the metal over a **sand bag** or **domed wooden block**, and hammer it with a **bossing mallet** (*Figure 5*). Move slowly round the piece, gradually working towards the centre. You may need to do this several times to achieve a good shape.

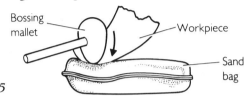

Figure 5

Annealing

Copper and aluminium sheets become harder as you hammer them. This is known as **work hardening.** You need to be able to soften them. This is done by **annealing.**

For copper, hold the piece of metal in a brazing hearth (*page 88*) and heat it to a cherry red colour. Then let it cool, or quench it in water. Place it in an acid bath (*page 80*) for a while. Remove it carefully, wash it in water and clean it with pumice powder.

For aluminium, first coat the metal with soap. The soap will show when the right temperature is reached. Heat the metal slowly until it goes black, then leave it to cool.

Annealing softens the material, which can then be hammered. When the material hardens, anneal it again. You can do this several times.

Finishing

Copper and aluminium can be finished by **planishing.** Hold the article on a **stake.** Start at the centre, and work outwards in a circular form, hammering the metal with a **planishing hammer**

Figure 6

(*Figure 6*). This is difficult to do well, and the stake and the hammer must be very smooth and polished. Planishing usually leaves small marks. These give a pleasant appearance, although you should aim to make a smooth surface.

Deforming plastics

Thermoplastics, such as acrylic, deform easily at low temperatures (about 160°C). You can solve many design problems by forming and reforming plastic.

The techniques shown here use a small oven or a strip heater. Do no use a gas oven. Use leather gloves when handling hot plastic! Most thermoplastics can be deformed in the same way as acrylic is shown here.

Deforming techniques

Making shapes in relief

When you heat acrylic, you can compress it. If you reheat it, it will go back to its original shape. This is called the **memory technique**. You can use this to make shapes that are raised from the surface of the plastic. Shapes that stick up in this way are said to be in **relief**.

Bend a piece of metal rod into the shape you want. Heat the acrylic until it is soft and pliable. Using a vice or book press, press the shaped metal rod into the acrylic, and hold it there until the plastic is cold (*Figure 1*). Now remove the metal shape. It will leave an indentation, the same shape as the rod.

To make this shape in relief, file away most of the surface. Leave just a small indentation (*Figure 2*). Reheat the plastic in the oven. The compressed part will return to its original size. The shape you designed will appear, raised from the surface (*Figure 3*). You can make this effect more striking by using matt and shiny surfaces together.

Bending along lines

You need a **strip heater** (*Figure 4*). Heat both sides of the acrylic along the line. Be careful not to overheat the plastic. Then bend the plastic to the required shape.

To make a simple 90° corner, just press the plastic into an angled **mould** (*Figure 5*). To make the shape of the corner more accurate, use a second mould. This could be a guide strip or a wooden block (*Figure 6*). Wooden moulds are covered with cotton sheet to prevent the grain from marking the plastic.

Bending into complex shapes

Three-dimensional forming of plastic is used to make small trays and dishes. Use acrylic of up to 3 mm thickness. You need to make a suitable mould.

Moulds are made in two parts (*Figure 7*). One part, the **plug**, has the shape in relief. The other part, the **yoke**, sits over the top of the plug. **Pins** are used to make sure that the parts come together accurately.

Heat the acrylic in an oven until it is pliable. Drape it over the plug, and press the yoke down on top (*Figure 8*). Hold the mould together until the plastic is cold. Then cut away the surplus plastic. Finish by shaping and polishing.

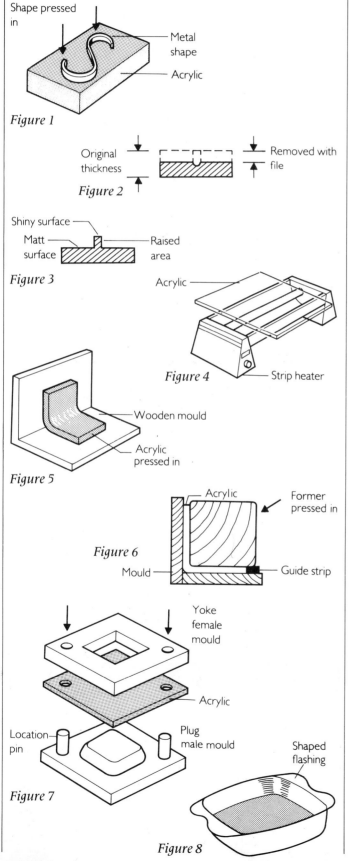

Figure 1

Figure 2

Figure 3

Figure 4

Figure 5

Figure 6

Figure 7

Figure 8

Deforming wood

Most kinds of timber can be deformed by applying force in some way. But when the force is removed, they normally return to their natural shape.

Deforming technique

Most wood is deformed by building up layers of thin pieces of wood (veneers). The veneers are glued together to the new shape. This process is called **laminating**. It makes the wood stronger than natural solid timber (*Figure 9*).

The materials used for laminating are as follows.

★ *Decorative veneers – these are expensive, and are used only on the outsides of shapes. Normally 1.0 mm to 1.5 mm thick.*
★ *Construction veneers – these are cheap and rotary cut from mahogany. Normally 1.0 mm to 2.5 mm thick.*
★ *Coloured veneers – good quality veneers stained particular colours. Normally 1.0 mm to 1.5 mm thick.*
★ *Thin plywood – this is already a combination of veneers. It may be up to 3 mm thick.*

Veneers are generally glued together with PVA. If the article is going to be soaked, use a special synthetic resin glue which is waterproof.

To deform and laminate wood you need a mould called a **former** (*Figure 10*). This is in two parts which fit together exactly. Place the veneers in the centre. Wrap polythene around them to stop them sticking to the former. Put sheets of rubber or cork between the polythene and the former. See Figure 11. Veneers, polythene, and rubber or cork should all be bigger than the mould.

Now cramp the former together *without gluing the veneers*. This is to see if the veneers bend easily. If not, dampen them and leave them overnight.

Glue the *whole surface* of each veneer. Place everything in the former and cramp this together. Squeeze it until the glue is forced out round the edges. You can use a vice to do this, but **sash cramps** are better (*Figure 12*). Leave the work overnight so that the glue sets.

Remove the work from the former. To finish it, make a template of the final shape you want. Stick the template to the laminate (*Figure 13*). Now cut round the template. Complete your work by smoothing the surface and treating it, as described on page 80.

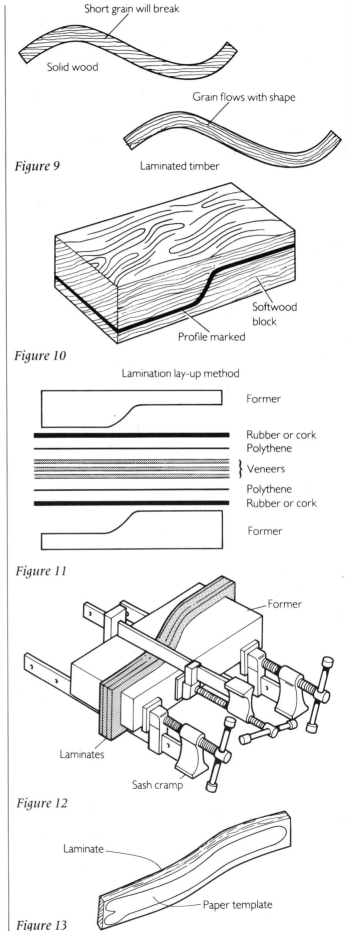

Figure 9

Short grain will break
Solid wood
Grain flows with shape
Laminated timber

Figure 10

Softwood block
Profile marked

Lamination lay-up method
Former
Rubber or cork
Polythene
Veneers
Polythene
Rubber or cork
Former

Figure 11

Former
Laminates
Sash cramp

Figure 12

Laminate
Paper template

Figure 13

Reforming

Plastics and metals can be cut to shape and bent to shape, as you have seen. They can also be **reformed**. Two common types of reforming are **casting** and **enamelling**. These are described below.

Casting

This book looks only at ways of casting plastic. Later books will look at ways of casting metal. Here we shall look at four processes:

* moulding
* surface coating
* embedding
* casting jewellery

Moulding

First design the form you want. Then find a small block of paraffin wax. Carefully carve out a *negative* copy of your design. In other words, make a hole into which your article would fit exactly.

Put sticky tape or plasticine round the block to keep it firm (*Figure 1*). Then prepare the polyester **resin**.

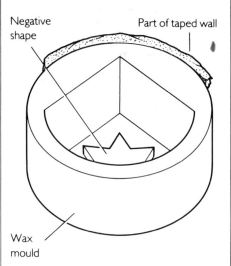

Figure 1

* *Get a special cup to mix the resin in. The cup may be waxed paper, PVC or polythene. It must not be polystyrene, as this dissolves in resin.*
* *Measure the amount of resin you need, and put it in the cup.*
* *Add pigment, if you wish, to colour the resin. Mix thoroughly.*
* *Add a hardener (catalyst) to the resin – usually 2%. Mix thoroughly.*
* *Pour the resin mixture into the wax mould. Leave it to harden.*
* *Clean the cup.*
* *When the resin has set remove the article from the mould and clean it.*

Embedding

Objects can be covered with resin to protect them. This is called **embedding** or **encapsulation**. You can use it to preserve things, to make small bases or projects like paperweights.

You need a smooth mould to get a good finish. Make sure there is no dust around.

* *Make up the resin as above excluding pigment.*
* *Put a layer in the bottom of the mould and let it stiffen (Figure 2). This will be the top of the embedded object.*

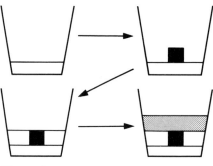

Figure 2

* *Put the object in the mould, on the layer of resin. Pour more resin around the object and over the top of it.*
* *You can fill the mould with clear resin if you wish. Or you can mix pigment into the resin so that the last layer is coloured. This will be the base of the coated object. Leave the resin to harden.*
* *When the resin has set, remove the article from the mould. Finish it by using wet-and-dry abrasive paper. Then polish it with a polishing paste.*

Surface coating

You can put a layer of resin onto chipboard or plywood. This is useful in making decorative boards for cheese, teapots and so on.

* *Start with a piece of chipboard that is slightly too big.*
* *Stick tape round the edge so that it forms a wall about 5 mm above the surface.*
* *Make sure that the board is absolutely horizontal.*
* *Mix enough resin to coat the surface. The resin layer should be about 2 mm thick. Add hardener, using slightly less than usual.*
* *Split the resin into several cups. Add different pigments to each of them. Mix each of them thoroughly. Note that the hardener is added before dividing the resin into cups. This makes sure that all the resin sets at the same speed.*
* *Pour the resin from the cups onto the chipboard. You can let the pattern flow naturally. Or you can use a sharpened piece of dowel to draw a pattern (Figure 3). Leave the resin to harden.*

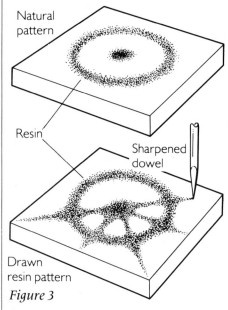

Figure 3

* *When the resin is set, remove the tape. Cut the board to size. Clean the edges of the board with a file and wet-and-dry papers. You can put iron-on veneer along the edges to finish the article.*

Reforming

Casting resin jewellery

You can make jewellery using the methods described on the opposite page. Here are some ideas.

★ *Put a surface coating onto a piece of three-ply. When it has set, find an interesting part of the pattern. Cut this out to a shape you have designed. You can use a template to help with this. If you need to drill a hole, drill it from the resin side. Clean the edges of the work. Put lacquer on the back and sides. See Figure 4.*

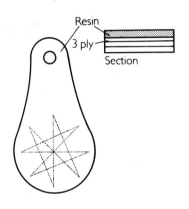

Figure 4

★ *Make a three-dimensional design. Use tinplate to make a suitable mould (Figure 5). You can soft-solder this if you wish (page 88). Put the mould on a tinplate base and seal the cracks with plasticine. Pour in the resin. Mix colour into it with a piece of dowel if you wish. When it has set, take it out of the mould. Finish by drilling and polishing.*

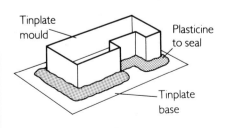

Figure 5

★ *For a better quality result, you can make the mould from copper, and silver-solder it. When the resin has set, you can leave the copper as an attractive frame for the jewellery.*

Enamelling

Enamel is glass, in a powder, in threads or in lumps. When you heat this to over 900°C, the enamel melts. Usually you apply enamels to the surface of metal, especially copper. Then when you melt the enamel, it fuses to the metal.

★ *Design a shape and cut it out of a sheet of copper.*
★ *Drill a hole, if you want one.*
★ *Clean and smooth the edges and surface of the copper blank.*
★ *Paint the surface with a thin layer of glue. Wallpaper paste is suitable.*
★ *Place the copper on a piece of paper. Sieve the enamel onto it (Figure 6). Leave the glue to dry.*

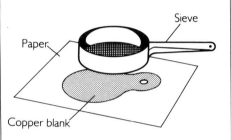

Figure 6

★ *Shake off the surplus enamel, and put it back in its container.*
★ *Place the copper on a wire mesh (Figure 7). Put this carefully into the hot kiln.*

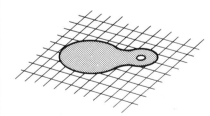

Figure 7

★ *Leave the copper for a few minutes until the enamel has melted and fused. Remove it from the kiln and let it cool. Warn other people that it is hot!*
★ *When it is cold, place it in an acid bath. (Wear eye protection!) This will remove the layer of oxide that has formed. Wash the article in water. Do not bend it – the enamel might crack.*

You can alter this technique in several ways.

★ *You can choose one colour for most of the object, and a different colour for part of it. One way of combining them is to put a lump of the second colour in among the powder of the first colour (Figure 8). When the enamel is melted, the colours will flow and fuse together.*

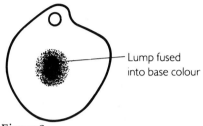

Figure 8

★ *You can trail the lump through the rest of the enamel while it is still molten (Figure 9). Be careful – everything will be very hot! Use a piece of wire to move the lump.*

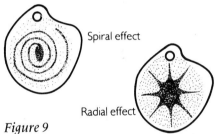

Figure 9

★ *Similarly, you can use a powder of one colour and some threads of another colour (Figure 10). Again, you can use a piece of wire to trail the threads over the object when the enamel is molten (Figure 11).*

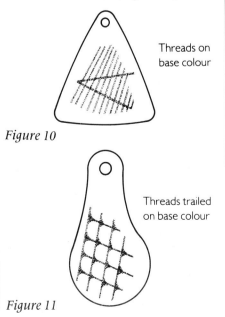

Figure 10

Figure 11

Joining

There are many different ways of joining pieces of material together. Here are just a few of them.

Nails

Nails are used to join pieces of wood together. They hold the wood by friction between wood and nail.

There are lots of types of nail. **Wire nails** are used for general work. **Oval nails** do not hold as securely as round nails, but are less likely to split the wood. **Panel pins** are used to pin flat sheets onto frames. See Figure 1.

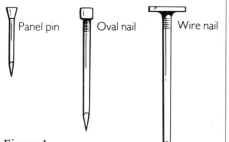

Figure 1

Here are some general points to remember.

★ *When you join a thicker piece of wood to a thinner piece, always nail through the thinner piece first.*

★ *Try not to put all the nails in a line. This may cause the wood to split. Instead, stagger them as in Figure 2.*

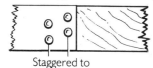
Staggered to prevent splitting

Figure 2

★ *To remove nails, use pincers (Figure 3). Always use a block of waste wood, to protect the piece with the nails in.*

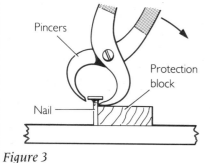
Pincers

Protection block

Nail

Figure 3

Screws

Screws are also used to join pieces of wood together. They are stronger than nails. The screws themselves are made of steel or brass. They compress the fibres of the wood. This strengthens the joint.

There are three types of screw head. One is domed, and sits above the surface. This is a **round head screw**. Another is flat on the top but bevelled below. This is sunk into the wood so that it sits level with the surface. This is the **countersink screw**. The third type of head is a combination of the other two. It stays slightly above the surface. It is known as a **raised head screw**. See Figure 4.

Screws are turned by means of a slot in the screw head. This may be straight or cross-shaped – posidrive (*Figure 5*). When you order screws, state the length, the shape of the head, the material, and the **gauge number** which indicates the diameter of the screws you want (*Figure 6*).

With hard wood, you need to prepare the hole before you put the screw in. If you don't, the wood will crack. First mark the position of the screw. Start the hole using a **bradawl**. Then drill a hole to fit the core diameter of the screw. Don't drill it too big or the screw won't hold! Drill the top part of the hole with a larger drill bit, to fit the shank of the screw. If you are using countersunk screws drill the countersink last. See Figure 7.

Some screws are made of hardened steel. They are used to join thin sheets of metal, some plastics, and chipboard. These screws cut their own thread in the material as they are screwed in. They are called **self-tapping screws** (*Figure 8*).

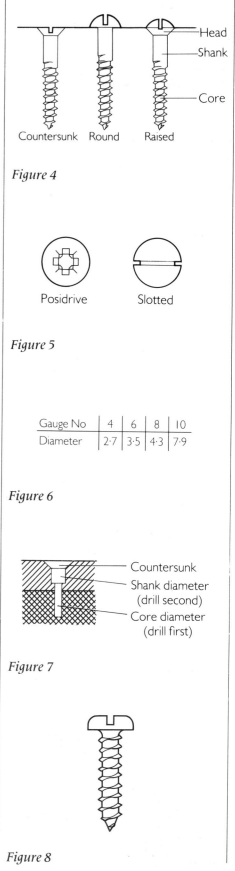

Countersunk   Round   Raised

Head
Shank
Core

Figure 4

Posidrive   Slotted

Figure 5

Gauge No	4	6	8	10
Diameter	2·7	3·5	4·3	7·9

Figure 6

Countersunk
Shank diameter (drill second)
Core diameter (drill first)

Figure 7

Figure 8

Joining

Nuts and bolts

Nuts and bolts are used to make joints that may need to be undone later. They may be made of steel or brass. Nuts and bolt heads may be square or hexagonal. Some bolts, called **machine screws**, have round heads with a straight or posidrive slot in them. All nuts and bolts have a thread (*Figure 9*). The thread on the nut must be the same as the thread on the bolt. Be careful to check this when you use them.

If you use a bolt, it is a good idea to put **washers** on both sides of the joint. Washers are usually flat, but there are also spring washers (*Figure 10*). Washers make the joint stronger.

Nuts may come loose if there is a lot of vibration. And sometimes you may not want to tighten the nut fully. You can solve both problems by using two nuts on the same bolt. Tighten them together with two spanners (*Figure 11*). The second nut is called a **locknut**. This is useful for holding wheels on axles.

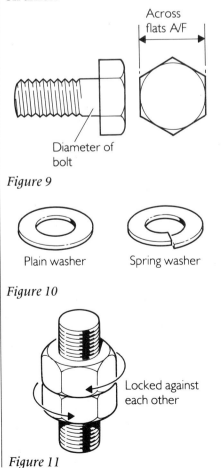

Figure 9

Plain washer   Spring washer

Figure 10

Locked against each other

Figure 11

Rivets

Rivets are used to join pieces of metal together. There are two kinds of rivet, solid and pop.

Solid rivets are usually made of mild steel. **Snap rivets** have domed heads (*Figure 12*). **Countersink rivets** sit level with the surface of the metal (*Figure 13*). Both are finished by hammering the other end of the rivet. Support snap rivets in a **dolly**, and hammer the other end using a **set** (*Figure 14*). Support countersink rivets on a flat surface, and hammer the other end into a countersunk hole on the back (*Figure 15*). These rivets give a strong permanent joint, but you need to get at both sides of the joint while riveting.

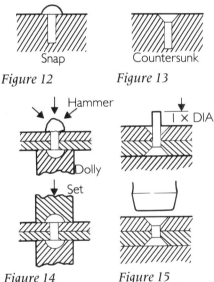

Snap   Countersunk

Figure 12   *Figure 13*

Hammer   DIA

Dolly   Set

Figure 14   *Figure 15*

Pop rivets are usually made of aluminium with a steel pin (*Figure 16*). First push the rivet through the hole. Then pull the pin back, using a **rivet gun** (*Figure 17*). The pin breaks. Sometimes a washer is used to support the rivet at the back. Pop rivets are quicker to use than solid rivets and can be operated from one side, but they do not give such a strong joint.

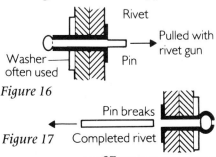

Rivet

Washer often used   Pin   Pulled with rivet gun

Figure 16

Pin breaks

Figure 17   Completed rivet

Adhesives

Many materials are joined together with glue, or **adhesive**. Joints are stronger if glue is used as well as a mechanical fixing, such as screws. But glues are often used by themselves.

Here are some guidelines for adhesives.

★ *Make sure the surfaces are clean and dry. There must be no grease, paint or lacquer on the surface.*

★ *Whenever possible, remove the shiny surface. But make sure that there is a close fit between the pieces you are joining.*

★ *After gluing, cramp the pieces together until the glue is dry. This makes the joint stronger.*

Metal Metals are rarely glued. Glue is sometimes necessary on clasps, brooch backs and similar articles. If you need to glue metal, use epoxy resin.

Plastic For *acrylic*, use Tensol cement. This comes in many forms. For *polystyrene*, use special polystyrene cement. For *expanded polystyrene*, use PVA glue or Copydex. For *PVC*, use vinyl adhesive (often called vinyl weld).

Wood The two most common wood glues are synthetic resin glue and polyvinyl acetate glue. **Synthetic resin glues** are waterproof and give a strong joint. They are colourless and set within four hours. They stain some woods. If not used immediately after mixing, they become unusable. Cascamite and Aerolite are two synthetic resin glues.

Polyvinyl acetate glues are white, liquid glues. They give strong joints. They do not stain wood. But these glues are not waterproof, so they must not be used for outdoor work. They are always ready to use. PVA and Resin W are two polyvinyl acetate glues.

Across flats A/F

Diameter of bolt

Joining

Soldering

Pieces of metal can be joined together with **solder**. Solder is an alloy. You melt it along the joint, and it cools and hardens, rather like a glue.

The solder itself is bought as a **filler rod**. As well as solder, you need a material called **flux**. This helps the molten solder to flow along the joint. Flux also prevents the metal from being oxidized. Metal oxides can spoil the appearance of your work.

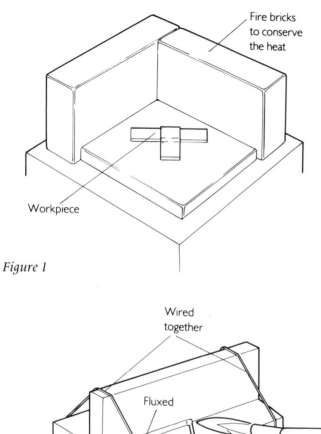

Figure 1

Figure 2

Hard soldering

To hard solder a joint, you need a gas torch. Air is blown with the gas, and this keeps the flame hot. Put fire bricks around your work when you do this (*Figure 1*). There are two types of hard soldering.

Brazing is used to join mild steel. The solder for brazing is called **spelter**. It is an alloy of copper and zinc.

Silver soldering is used to join copper or brass. The solder for this is an alloy of silver, copper and zinc. Different proportions of these metals are used to make solders which melt at different temperatures.

Both types of hard soldering use the same technique. Both use **borax** flux.

★ *Fasten the workpiece together using soft iron wire.*
★ *Some powdered flux is mixed into a paste. Arrange some paste flux around the joint.*
★ *Light the torch carefully. Adjust it to get a gentle flame.*
★ *Play the flame over the workpiece. The flux will bubble and then settle.*
★ *Increase the temperature until the workpiece is red hot.*
★ *Warm the solder, which is a rod. Stick this into the flux powder.*
★ *Apply the solder rod to the joint (Figure 2). The rod will melt along the workpiece, and run along and through the joint (Figure 2).*
★ *Leave the workpiece to cool and then clean it.*

Soft soldering

To soft solder a joint, you need a heated copper bit. This type of soldering is done at a much lower temperature than hard soldering. Soft soldering is used for tin plate, copper, brass and occasionally mild steel. The joints produced are weaker than the ones produced by hard soldering. Note that you cannot solder aluminium.

For flux, use **Baker's fluid**. This is made of zinc chloride, which is corrosive. Be very careful when you handle it. For solder, use Tinman's solder. This is an alloy of equai amounts of tin and lead.

★ *Fasten the workpiece together using soft iron wire.*
★ *Heat a large electrical soldering iron (Figure 3). (You can use a copper bit heated in a gas stove.) Copper holds heat well.*
★ *When the iron is hot, clean the end. Use an old file to do this.*
★ *Put some flux on the bit. Then add solder. Slowly coat the bit with solder in this way. This process is called **tinning**.*
★ *Apply the bit to the joint on the workpiece. Run the solder along the joint slowly. Tin the end again when necessary.*
★ *Let the joint cool slowly. Then wash the flux off with water.*

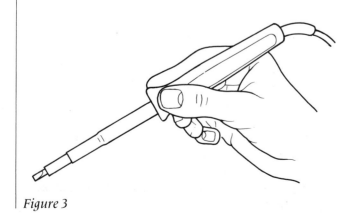

Figure 3

Joining

Soldering electronic components

When you use electronic components, you often need to solder them together. You must do this with care, so that the solder flows in the right places.

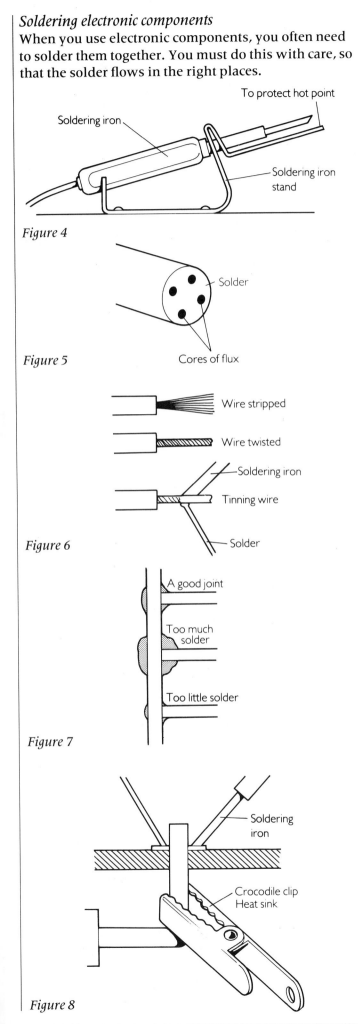

Figure 4

Figure 5

Figure 6

Figure 7

Figure 8

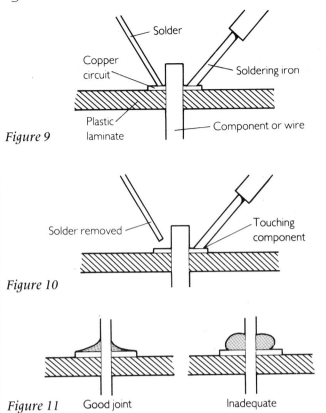

Figure 9

Figure 10

Figure 11   Good joint   Inadequate

Use a 15-watt electrical soldering iron. Keep this on a stand when you are not using it (*Figure 4*). Use a special soft solder. This is an alloy of tin and lead. It melts at low temperatures. The flux is a resin which is not corrosive. Flux and solder are combined in one soft wire, so they are easy to use (*Figure 5*).

★ *Clean and tin the bit on the soldering iron, as above.*
★ *Components are usually tinned when bought. If your components are not tinned, tin them (Figure 6).*
★ *Use wire strippers to remove the insulation from your wires. Tin the ends of the wires.*
★ *Before soldering a joint, make a mechanical joint. Do this by bending the wires together. Be careful not to break strands off the wire. Be careful also not to break the leads off the components.*
★ *To solder the joint, hold the solder one side and the soldering iron the other.*
★ *Remove the soldering iron and leave the joint still for a moment to set. See Figure 7.*

You need to be especially accurate when you solder components to printed circuits. If you are not careful, you may make a short circuit.

★ *Feed the component leads through the circuit board.*
★ *Fit a* **heat sink** *between the component and the point where the soldering iron will be used (Figure 8). This protects the component from the heat.*
★ *Apply the heat of the soldering iron to the copper strip, not to the component (Figure 9).*
★ *Remove the solder when it begins to melt (Figure 10). Then move the soldering iron to touch the component's wire for a few seconds.*
★ *Put the solder back on the joint to complete the soldering. See Figure 11.*

Joining

Constructional joints

A constructional joint is a method of holding together material. The strength of these joints varies. If mechanical interlocking takes place and is combined with glue a very strong joint is made. Constructional joints are usually used with wood, because you cannot join wood by using heat. Constructional joints can be difficult to make.

Before you join two pieces of wood, think about these questions.

* ★ *What shape do you want?*
* ★ *How strong must the joint be? Which way will the forces act?*
* ★ *What must the finished job look like? You may not want the ends of the wood grain to show.*
* ★ *What are the properties of the wood you are using?*
* ★ *How big a surface can be glued? Note that end grain does not glue well.*

There are two basic types of jointing wood, box joints and frame joints. Choose your joint from the ones given here. Remember to mark out the joint very carefully. Interlocking pieces of wood must fit exactly.

Box joints
There are lots of different joints used in making boxes.

Butt joint   This is the simplest form of corner joint (*Figure 1*). It is rather weak. You can strengthen a butt joint by nailing the pieces at an angle (*Figure 2*). Or you can add a corner block (*Figure 3*).

Figure 1

Dovetail nailing

Figure 2

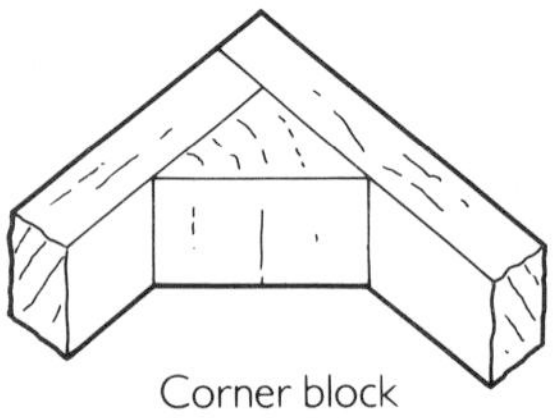

Corner block

Figure 3

Mitre joint   This is also a corner joint (*Figure 4*). It hides all the end grain. It also gives a bigger surface to glue, but the surface is end grain and this is difficult to glue well. Cut the mitre using a mitre box (*Figure 5*).

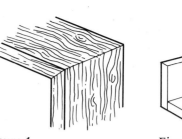

Figure 4

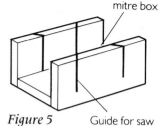

Wood in mitre box

Figure 5

Guide for saw

This keeps the saw cuts at 45°. You can strengthen a mitre joint by cutting a slot and inserting a piece of veneer (*Figure 6*).

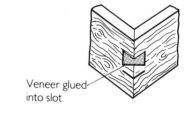

Veneer glued into slot

Figure 6

Rebate or **lapped joint**   Another corner joint. This needs two saw cuts (*Figure 7*). It is stronger than a butt joint, but some end grain shows. You should glue this joint. Rebate joints can be strengthened with pins.

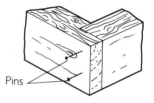

Pins

Figure 7

Tongue and groove joint   This is also a corner joint (*Figure 8*). One piece of wood has a groove in it. You need to saw and then chisel this. The other piece of wood has a matching tongue. You can make this with a saw. The tongue and groove joint absorbs pressure in both directions, so it is stronger than the rebate joint. But some end grain shows, and the end grain may break.

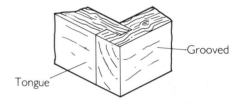

Grooved

Tongue

Figure 8

Housing joint   This is T-shaped but still a corner joint. Part of the wood sticks out (*Figure 9*). You can make a housing joint easily with a saw and chisel.

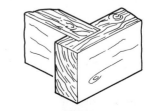

Figure 9

Joining

Dowelled joint This corner joint is a strengthened butt joint (*Figure 10*). Mark it out carefully. Drill the two pieces of wood at the same time, so that the holes match exactly. Use a dowelling jig to guide the drill (*Figure 11*). Glue the two dowelling pegs in position. The ends of these pegs show. This may look untidy. You can make the same kind of joint using shorter pegs (*Figure 12*). Drill only halfway through the lap. Drill from what will be the inside of the joint. (You can use the same dowelling jig, provided this is symmetrical.) This kind of dowelled joint is tidier, but not as strong. It needs great care when marking out and drilling.

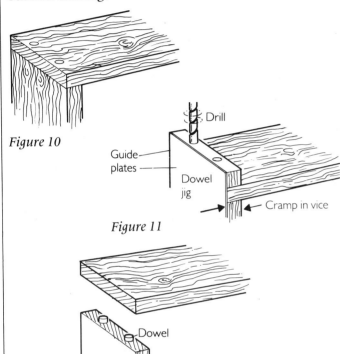

Figure 10

Figure 11

Figure 12

Dovetail joints There are many different dovetail joints. Here is just one of them (*Figure 13*). This is called the **through dovetail**. It has great mechanical strength and a large gluing surface.

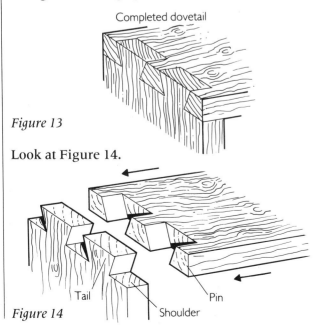

Completed dovetail

Figure 13

Look at Figure 14.

Figure 14

Notice that there are **pins**, **tails** and **shoulders**. Both pin and tail are tapered. The thinnest bit of the tail is slightly bigger than the thickest bit of the pin. The slope of the taper may be from 1 to 6 (for softwoods) to 1 in 8 (for hardwoods) (*Figure 15*).

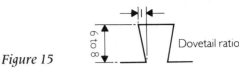

Dovetail ratio

Figure 15

★ *Mark this joint out very carefully.*
★ *Always cut the tails first. Place the tail piece of wood in the vice. Saw the four slopes. Then cut the shoulders. Cut the centre piece with a chisel.*
★ *Now place the pin piece of wood in the vice. Use the tail piece to help you mark out the pin piece. Saw the pins. Chisel away the waste wood between the pins.*
★ *Check that the joint fits together and holds firmly.*
★ *Clean the inside surfaces.*
★ *Glue all surfaces and fit the joint together.*

Now look at the joints all together (*Figure 16*). Make sure you understand how each works. The diagram shows where joints are strong and where they are weak. You should think about this when you choose a joint.

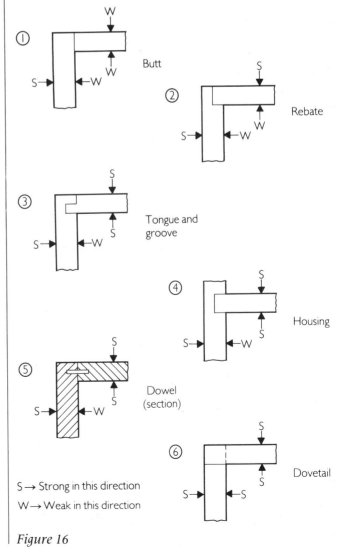

① Butt
② Rebate
③ Tongue and groove
④ Housing
⑤ Dowel (section)
⑥ Dovetail

S → Strong in this direction
W → Weak in this direction

Figure 16

Joining

Frame joints

Frame joints make structures more rigid. You need them for chairs, windows and so on. On these two pages there are some simple frame joints. You can use these for picture frames, racks, and boxes covered with plywood, for example.

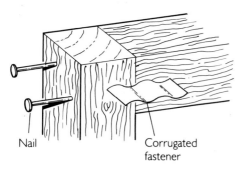

Nail

Corrugated fastener

Figure 1

Butt joint This is a weak joint. In a frame it can be strengthened with a corrugated fastener. Or it may be pinned (*Figure 1*). The joint may be covered with plywood to give strength.

Mitre joint This is used a lot for picture frames. You can pin the joint to strengthen it (*Figure 2*).

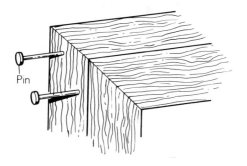

Pin

Figure 2

Corner-halving joint This simple joint can be made with four saw cuts (*Figure 3*).
End grain shows on both sides of the joint. The corner-halving is quite strong, and has a large gluing surface. The joint can be strengthened with nails or dowel.

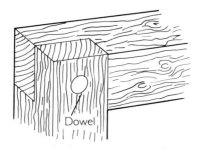

Dowel

Figure 3

Dowelled joint This is strong, neat and tidy (*Figure 4*). The dowelling joint is made as shown on page 91.

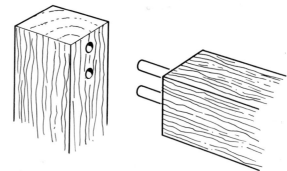

Figure 4

Corner bridle joint This joint is strong (*Figure 5*). One piece of wood has a part that sticks out, the **tenon**. The other piece of wood has a matching slot, the **mortise**. Make the tenon by sawing.

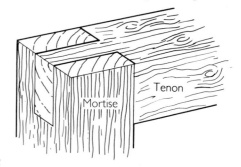

Tenon

Mortise

Figure 5

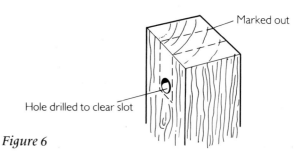

Marked out

Hole drilled to clear slot

Figure 6

Make the mortise by drilling near the base of the slot (*Figure 6*). Then saw down the edges and remove the waste. Clean the bottom of the mortise using a chisel. You can strengthen this joint still more with dowel.

Tee-halving joint This is a bit like the corner-halving joint. Compare Figure 7 with Figure 3. The tee-halving joint is useful for light frames.

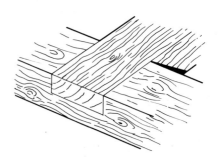

Figure 7

Joining

Dovetail halving joint   This joint can withstand pressure in both directions (*Figure 8*). Use the same basic method as for the dovetail joint on page 91.

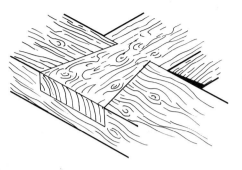

Figure 8

Cross-halving joint   This joint is for use where two pieces of wood cross (*Figures 9 and 10*). It is made like the corner-halving joint (*Figure 3*) and the tee-halving joint (*Figure 7*). Again, you can use dowel to make the joint stronger.

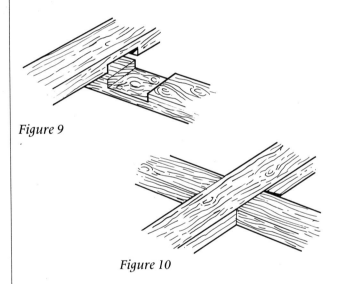

Figure 9

Figure 10

Special joints

Apart from the mechanical joints shown above, there are some special ones that may be useful.

Corner joints   One common new fitting is a plastic block in two parts (*Figure 11*). The parts of the block are screwed to the pieces of wood, commonly chipboard. Then a machine screw is used to pull the parts of the block together.

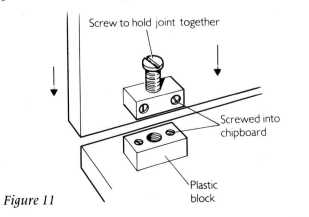

Screw to hold joint together

Screwed into chipboard

Plastic block

Figure 11

Another kind of fitting uses a nylon plug (*Figure 12*). Drill a hole to fit the plug, and push the plug into this. Drill a slightly smaller hole through the other piece of wood. Put a screw through this hole and into the nylon plug.

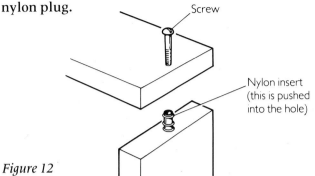

Screw

Nylon insert (this is pushed into the hole)

Figure 12

Axles   You often need to put wheels on a workpiece. There are some modern kits to help with this.

One simple way of attaching wheels uses a screw as a **static axle** (*Figure 13*). Drill the wheel making a hole slightly bigger than the screw, so that the wheel can turn easily. Put washers each side of the wheel to prevent wear. The hole in the wheel will get bigger with time, so this is not a very satisfactory method.

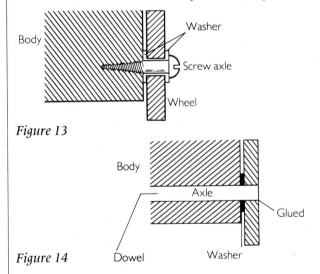

Body

Washer

Screw axle

Wheel

Figure 13

Body

Axle

Glued

Figure 14   Dowel   Washer

You can use a piece of dowel glued to the wheel. The dowel passes through a hole in the body of the object (*Figure 14*). This **moving axle** lasts longer than the screw. But the axle breaks easily. Another method is to use a bolt and locknuts (*Figure 15*). You can place the locknuts where you want them, so you can decide how easily the wheel turns. If one axle goes through the object, bolt it at both sides.

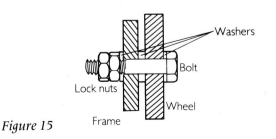

Washers

Bolt

Lock nuts

Frame

Wheel

Figure 15

Note that you will find the hole saw (*page 78*) useful when you make wheels.

Funny-face toy

These two pages show the result of one project. They show one solution to a set problem. The design brief was this:

Using the materials provided (6 + 12 mm dowel rod and plywood 210 × 150 × 6 mm), design and construct a 'funny-face toy' that includes a mechanical movement.

Look at the result. Ask yourself these questions.

★ *Did the designer analyse the design brief fully?*
★ *Did she carry out any research?*
★ *Did she record her ideas on paper?*
★ *Did she think about the presentation of her design ideas?*
★ *Did she make working models?*
★ *Did she finish her work to a high standard?*
★ *Did she solve the problem set?*
★ *What would you do differently?*
★ *How would you tackle this project?*

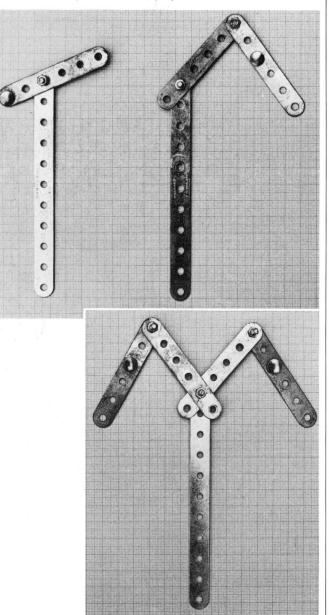

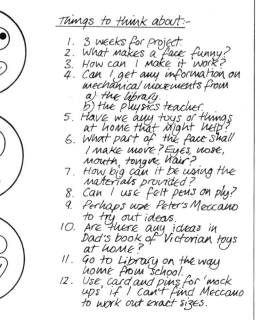

Design Brief :- Using the materials provided (6+12 mm dowl rod and plywood 210 x 150 x 6 mm) design and construct a funny face toy that includes a mechanical movement.

happy

sad

cross-eyed

Things to think about :-

1. 3 weeks for project.
2. What makes a face funny?
3. How can I make it work?
4. Can I get any information on mechanical movements from
   a) the library.
   b) the physics teacher.
5. Have we any toys or things at home that might help?
6. What part of the face shall I make move? Eyes, nose, mouth, tongue, hair?
7. How big can it be using the materials provided?
8. Can I use felt pens on ply?
9. Perhaps use Peter's Meccano to try out ideas.
10. Are there any ideas in Dad's book of Victorian toys at home?
11. Go to Library on the way home from school.
12. Use card and pins for 'mock ups' if I can't find Meccano to work out exact sizes.

SHEET 1.   Christine Godfrey   1p

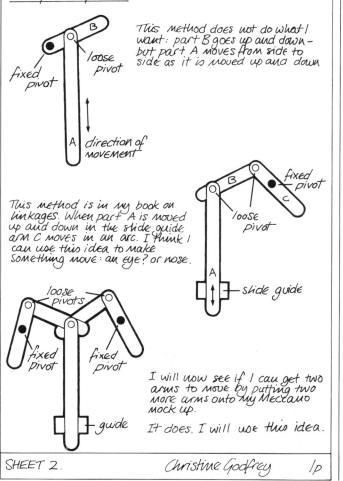

Development of Ideas Mechanical movements.

This method does not do what I want: part B goes up and down - but part A moves from side to side as it is moved up and down

fixed pivot

loose pivot

direction of movement

This method is in my book on linkages. When part A is moved up and down in the slide guide arm C moves in an arc. I think I can use this idea to make something move: an eye? or nose.

fixed pivot

loose pivot

slide guide

loose pivots

fixed pivot   fixed pivot

guide

I will now see if I can get two arms to move by putting two more arms onto my Meccano mock up.

It does. I will use this idea.

SHEET 2.   Christine Godfrey   1p

---94---

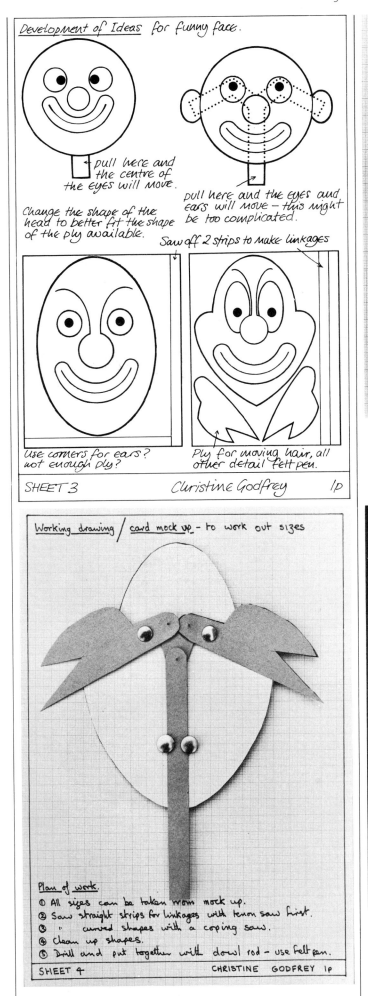

Development of Ideas for funny face.

← pull here and the centre of the eyes will move.

pull here and the eyes and ears will move — this might be too complicated.

Change the shape of the head to better fit the shape of the ply available.

Saw off 2 strips to make linkages

Use corners for ears? not enough ply?

Ply for moving hair, all other detail felt pen.

SHEET 3   Christine Godfrey   1p

Working drawing / card mock up — to work out sizes

Plan of work.
① All sizes can be taken from mock up.
② Saw straight strips for linkages with tenon saw first.
③ " curved shapes with a coping saw.
④ Clean up shapes.
⑤ Drill and put together with dowel rod — use felt pen.

SHEET 4   CHRISTINE GODFREY 1p

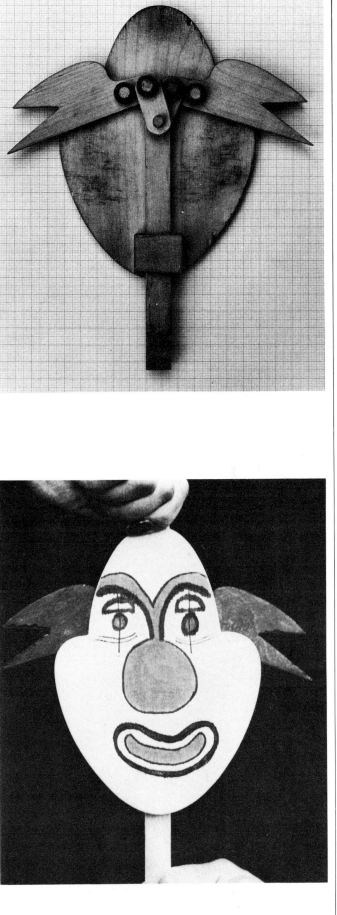

On the next four pages there are some design briefs. They are only suggestions. You or your teacher may like to change them. You might not have the necessary equipment at school. Or you might like to do something you've already thought of.

These suggestions should help you in the following ways:

★ *You can check what you know.*
★ *You can practise using tools.*
★ *You can practise techniques.*
★ *You can think about the technology of designs.*
★ *You can think about the appearance of designs.*
★ *You can practise drawing ideas on paper and making working models.*

1

Watch out for notes and pictures that help you with design. Match them to the sections in this book. Make sure you can find information from them when you want it.

2

* Use a smoothing plane to make shavings. They should all be the same thickness. Use a piece of timber that is 200 x 50 x 10 mm.
* Laminate the shavings round cylindrical objects. You could use pencils, or pens, or cigar tubes, or washing-up liquid bottles.
* Dye the laminated units in cold-water dye. Use colours that will harmonize.
* Use the dyed units to make a stylized figure or an animal or a bird. Or make a mobile with asymmetric balance.

3

* Take a piece of softwood 200 x 150 x 20 mm. Use a coping saw to make a stylized animal shape. Burn the surface of the wood. Then brush it with a wire brush. This will show the texture of the timber.
* The shape can be used as a printing block. Make a handle to hold it for this. The handle must be comfortable to hold.

4

* Take a piece of material 1500 x 15 x 8 mm. Saw 80 mm units from this. Make as many units as possible.
* Use the units to make a sculpture. The sculpture should show movement or rhythm.

5

You need a piece of 3 mm plywood and a piece of hardboard. Both are A4 size. Design and make a jigsaw to help a child learn some new words. For example, the words could be eye, mouth, tail, or round, square, triangular. You choose the words.

6

You have dowel (150 x 5 mm), timber (300 x 50 x 25 mm) and 6 plywood wheels or beads. Design and build a toy for a young child. The toy must have at least two moving parts.

7

Laminate and shape a piece of acrylic to make a paperweight. The paperweight must be attractive to look at and to hold. Use harmonizing or contrasting colours.

8

* Study the linear patterns in nature. Look at aerial views of rivers. Look at reflections on water. Look at sections of timber. Look at the stripes on animals. What else can you find?
* Now use these patterns. Make something by etching, or by using the heat memory of acrylic.

10

Make the tallest possible structure using a copy of yesterday's newspaper. The structure must stand by itself. You can use up to 500 mm of masking tape.

9

Design and construct a paper structure. Use only one sheet of A4 typing paper. The structure must be able to support as much weight as possible. The weight must be at least 50 mm from the base.

11

Use tinned wire to make a two-dimensional face. The face may be happy or sad.

12

Design and make a punch. The punch will be used to emboss a piece of 3 mm leather, to make a key fob or hair slide. You can use a 10 mm square section of mild steel. You must include one circle (made by drilling) and up to three lines (made by sawing). How many repeat variations are possible with one punch?

13

You have a piece of timber that is 180 x 75 x 50 mm. Design a candle shade that will make interesting shadows. Use a brace and bit and through housings. Your teacher will slice the block into four pieces for you.

14

You have one A4 size piece of 3 mm plywood, 4 nuts and bolts and a piece of nylon thread. Make a stylized clown. His arms and legs must move by pulling on the nylon thread.

15

Use timber (650 x 50 x 25 mm) to make an interlocking toy for a 5 year-old child. Include one cross-halving joint, and one mortise-and-tenon joint.

16

Make a mechanical toy money box that works when you put a coin in a slot.

17

Make a vehicle that will move as far as possible, using 500 g silver sand as the source of energy.

18

Make an article for storing things in a bathroom. Use 3 mm acrylic sheet. Use the line bending technique. Your teacher will tell you how big the acrylic sheet is.

19

Design and build a game for
a 12 year-old on a journey.
The game must be nice to
hold.
* Make it in a vacuum-formed
box. The box must be no
bigger than 120 x 80 x
50 mm.
* The design should use one
of the tecnniques used
with acrylic - heat
memory, dyeing, bending,
cementing or drilling.

20

Design a piece of
jewellery. It should
be based on a design
found in nature. Use
one of these tech-
niques - etching,
casting, enamelling,
laminating veneers.

21

Use tinned
iron wire to
make an
abstract
three-
dimensional
form that
shows speed.

22

Use a 10 x 1.5 mm mild steel
strip. You can choose the
length, wire and wheels
of your own choice. Make
a vehicle that travels
as far as possible using
the power from one
elastic band.

23

Use material
provided by your
teacher to make a
structure. The
structure should
make a noise when
a ball bearing
rolls over or
through it.

24

Visit a home for the
elderly, or a school
for the handicapped,
or a play group. Find
a problem that you
think you can solve.
For example, you might
make a toy for a child
who can't control his
fingers fully. Or you
might make a device to
help hold things. Make
your own design brief
and then work through
it.